Tensions
Our Children Live With

Tensions

Our Children Live With

Stories for Discussion

Edited by DOROTHY T. SPOERL

BEACON PRESS   BOSTON

Acknowledgments

I would like to acknowledge the help of many people who have contributed in varying ways to this volume: the help of the authors with their patient willingness to revise until a consistent point of view was achieved in spite of their great diversity of background and interest; the help of the members of the Curriculum Committee, the Editors, and the Staff, of the Council of Liberal Churches, who read each story with care and contributed detailed criticisms; the help of those who told these stories to classes in many sections of the country so that we could have the benefit of the reactions of groups of children, especially Mrs. Herbert Bloch, Baldwin, Long Island, Mr. Winslow Wetherbee, Stoughton, Massachusetts, and Mrs. Aldine B. Lisle, Charlottesville, Virginia; the help of those who criticized individual stories or groups of stories in which they had special interest — Mrs. Thelma Keitlen of the Anti-Defamation League, Dr. Mary Cannon McLean of the Springfield, Massachusetts Public Schools, Dr. Albert Schrekinger of the School of Social Work, University of Nebraska, Miss Ruth Griffith, at that time editor of the Labor Paper at the Monsanto Chemical Company, Springfield, Massachusetts, Mr. James Brennan of the American International College Counselling Center, and Mrs. Gordon W. Allport, Cambridge, Massachusetts.

A very special acknowledgment must be made to Mrs. Florence Klaber of the American Ethical Union and Dr. Lucile Lindberg of the Council of Liberal Churches' Editorial Staff and Queens College for their help in devising the questions for discussion that are supplied for each story, and to the Rev. Donald Harrington of the Community Church of New York from whose request for materials of this sort the whole project grew.

DOROTHY T. SPOERL

Contents

V. The broken family

VI. Children of different national, racial, or religious backgrounds

VII. Issues stemming from the adult community that affect the child

Introduction

Tensions Our Children Live With is an anthology of stories to
be used as a resource book by teachers who want either to raise the
specific problem with which a story deals or who would like to introduce a unit on problems of social relationships. It is not intended
as a course of study. Neither is it intended as a collection of stories
for worship services, although some of them might be so used. These
stories are planned primarily for the purpose of arousing discussion
and involving children in a consideration of the problems which are
found in the social relationships within a community.

The stories have been written so that the book as a whole covers
a wide age range, some of the stories being for children as young
as third graders, and some of them having been written with the
sixth grader in mind. In their experimental form they were found
to arouse interest among junior high school students. If a story con-
taining a particular problem that the teacher wishes to present is
written at an age level different from that of the children in the
class, the wording of the story can easily be changed in the telling
of it. As a matter of fact, age levels for stories are almost meaning-
less, as anyone knows who has told stories to an audience having
a wide range of ages.

Some of the stories in this collection are complete units; solutions are suggested within the story itself. Others are open-ended
stories, specifically planned so that the class will itself find and
discuss the solutions ("endings," the children will call them), which
have been purposely left up in the air. There are some teachers who
prefer using one type, and others who prefer another. But adaptation
is again possible, for the teacher may either supply endings if none
is given, or omit endings in the stories which are complete units.
We are primarily interested in the thinking process behind the
discussion of the wide variety of solutions which are possible. Obvi-
ously the class need not agree on a solution. Disagreement tends to
promote good discussion!

WHEN TO USE THE STORIES

There are many situations in which stories of this type may fit into your program. We shall consider here a few typical instances, to which many of you will have additions.

1. When a problem exists, which has not come out into the open, or when you want to avoid the personal issues that otherwise would be involved:

Many times a teacher is aware of an undercurrent of misunderstanding or lack of sympathy existing among the children in a class. Perhaps she has had reported to her instances of misunderstanding, segregation of other children for reasons of race, religion, etc., or has heard comments from the children about situations similar to those discussed in this book. Although, when possible, the real life situation is basically better for discussion purposes, it is not desirable to start by saying, "I understand that Jimmy is refusing to play with the little Jewish boy who has just moved into his neighborhood," or, "I see that you do not understand why Janie's father is out on strike." In this kind of situation, the introduction of a story may make possible the desired discussion, and, more important, will sometimes bring the child in question to the point where he may be able to say, "Oh, I didn't realize it, but that is just what I have been doing."

2. When you know the problem is going to come up, and would like to discuss it before it does become an issue:

The teacher may be aware that there is to be a strike in town; that migrant children are going to be introduced into the schools; that a couple who have been divorced are about to enter their child in the group; that a handicapped child is about to come into the class; or that a family which speaks a foreign language will move into the community. A full discussion and understanding of these problems before the situation actually arises will help clear the air and may make it possible to avoid unpleasant situations that need not arise.

3. When you feel that the class has not developed the kind of "social conscience" that children should have:

Many children have had so little experience with the way other people live that they have no basis for understanding or for the development of sympathy. Here again the discussion of these stories will help. A social conscience does not develop in a vacuum, and when the problems do not actually exist within the child's experience, their presentation in story form can often make the children aware of problems they would not meet otherwise. Above all, we want to avoid in our children the development of glib platitudes and to help them think through their ideas and feelings on these problems. Otherwise we cannot hope to build a generation of socially aware liberals.

4. When you want a short unit to finish out a term, or to fill in when materials are lacking, or when similar emergencies arise:

A prolonged discussion over a year's time of stories only of this kind would not, in many instances, be desirable for children. But if a course of study is finished, or has proven not to appeal to the children at all, or if the teacher is waiting for necessary materials before starting new work, here is material from which a teacher may choose problems to discuss over a period of a month or six weeks. In some instances, through this discussion, a whole unit of work on a special problem may develop out of the children's interest and ideas. Many of these problems are of deepest importance in our society. This is, of course, what a "child-centered curriculum" really means: the development of abiding interest out of an experience, real or vicarious. When such a situation does arise it is often a rich experience for children and teacher alike.

5. When a teacher has not planned work for a substitute, and no one really knows what the work should be:

Sometimes in a last-minute emergency a substitute teacher is left with a class about whose work she knows nothing. Instead of floundering about and breaking the real continuity of what the regular teacher was planning to do, it would be possible to introduce a problem. In this way the substitute could make valuable use of the time and could furthermore select an area in which her sympathy and knowledge were strong enough that a directed discussion would be possible even when there had not been time for adequate preparation.

Teachers will often find that outside reading on an adult level is needed before they feel ready to tackle some of these problems, but for each individual teacher there are probably areas in which she has already done the outside reading and thinking which are needed.

6. *When the children come in excited over a problem of which you had not realized they were aware:*

If the teacher has browsed through this book, and knows the

problem areas covered, she will often realize in the children's pre-class discussion that one of these very problems has become relevant to the children. She can stop the sometimes gossipy nature of this general discussion by saying, "I know of a story that tells about some people who had just that kind of problem. Would you like me to read it to you so that we can talk about it?"

Frequently teachers bypass the opportunity to teach from the life experience of the child, because, although the teacher recognizes that the experience is present, he can not on the spur of the moment think of a wholesome and stimulating way to present it to the class. It is hoped that this anthology may be useful in such instances.

7. *When the class has proven to be poor at discussion, and you feel that a little experience in this area would enrich the teaching for the balance of the year:*

Some of our children come to us from schools where discussion is a constant method in the classroom; others have had almost no opportunity for this kind of experience. If the teacher sees that the text to be used requires this ability and that the children have not developed it, these stories could be used for that purpose. (See number 3 under "Ways in Which the Stories May be Used" for further discussion of this point.)

8. *When the children have not touched upon a unit of work that you hoped would come up naturally, it may be possible to use these stories to introduce that unit:*

Perhaps your school is in an area where migrant workers are considered to be "a difficult problem"; or where segregation has been encouraged; or where children who attend a different church are misunderstood.

In situations of this kind, and others, the use of some of these stories may arouse the interest of the children to the point that they will ask (as you have been hoping they would), "Miss Jones, couldn't we really study this and find out more about it?" However, do not assume that every time such stories are used the children will demand more material! It is only when their interest is really captivated that they will demand more, and we must be patient and wait until such a time comes. But there is no reason why we cannot attempt on several occasions to rouse this interest if we feel that it is important for the children.

9. *When you are going to introduce the children into situations similar to those in these stories, then the story may serve as preparation for the experience which is to follow:*

Instead of allowing some of the opinions and attitudes of the story characters to develop, try using the stories in this collection before it is possible for the children to have some of the experiences described. This might be in a situation where a giving and sharing project is to be started and the teacher wants the children to go into the project with wholesome attitudes and values. Perhaps the children are going to share an experience with children of other races and creeds, and the teacher is not quite sure what their attitudes really are.

Before a field trip, a project, or a new situation, there is always value in a thorough discussion of the area to be experienced or observed. This adds real meaning to the experience itself and leads to more worthwhile discussion after the project has been completed.

10. When a film strip or a moving picture is going to be presented, the use of some of these stories may help develop "readiness" for the audio-visual aid:

One problem with audio-visual aids is that sometimes the teacher assumes that children have more sensitivity to, or knowledge about, situations than they really possess. When this happens the audio-visual presentation sometimes does not achieve the ends desired. This might be especially important, for instance, when a film or film-strip is to be used in an assembly or worship service. Children always get more from these experiences if the preparation for them has been as extensive as possible.

WAYS IN WHICH THE STORIES MAY BE USED

Naturally one does not just read the story, or better yet tell it, and then stop short at the end and wait hopefully for a worthwhile discussion to ensue. There are times when this may happen, but there are also times when it will not.

There are a number of ways in which stories such as these can be used. When discussion does not come from the group freely and easily, the teacher may experiment with some of these methods until she finds which is the most successful for her particular group. Each group is different, and each group therefore responds to differing methods of presentation. The teacher will think of many ways other than the sample methods which we have included here.

1. Telling the story, and just "letting the discussion happen":

In the experimental use of these stories a number of teachers reported that the children were not always willing to wait for the story to end before they started interrupting with comments on what should have been done, what could have been done, or what was wrong about the way in which the story characters handled the situation. If you have a group which is as eager as this to discuss and argue, you are a fortunate teacher. But, again, not all groups will react in this way.

2. Telling the story and asking each child to write or tell an ending of his own in the case of the open-ended stories; or asking the children to write a new ending for the story if you have presented the story as a completed unit:

Sometimes children find it difficult to accept the idea that there are a number of right ways to handle a single situation. If one occasionally tells an open-ended story, giving the child an opportunity to finish it, or if one occasionally asks for a new ending from each child, this will certainly show the group that there are as many solutions as there are individuals. Subsequent discussion will show that there is often no single "right" or "wrong" way to handle the situation.

This is a basic understanding that is of great value to children. It frees them from overdependence on adult values and standards and helps them to see that there are a wide variety of ways in which to look at almost any problem. It is important that children do not develop the idea that they have found *the* right way to behave, and that they not feel that theirs is the *only* way.

3. Letting the children start a discussion and then by skillful handling lead it first in one direction and then in another, so that it will have both greater width and depth than the children alone could give it:

For the teacher who feels insecure about this situation, there is a pamphlet, *Developing Quality in Discussion,* published by the Council of Liberal Churches, which will prove both comforting and helpful. We list the basic points from this pamphlet for quick reference and review, but suggest that each teacher using the stories secure a copy of the pamphlet itself.[1] There are certain abilities the teacher will need. She must have the ability to:

a. Be aware of long-term goals.
b. Listen to what the children say.

---

[1] Lindberg, Lucile. *Developing Quality in Discussion.* Department of Education, Council of Liberal Churches, 25 Beacon Street, Boston 8, Mass. Another pamphlet, *The Teacher's Role in Discussion,* is also available from the Council.

c. Explore with children.
d. Learn to recognize the values our children actually hold and not be shocked when they are inadequate.
e. Accept the children's own terminology and avoid the temptation to rephrase what they say in adult terms.
f. Encourage the children to examine.
g. Recognize the questions the children can not ask.
h. Ask the general reactions from everyone.
i. Recognize the questions for which there are no answers.
j. Clarify the children's ideas and introduce facts when they are needed.
k. Permit generalizations to develop.
l. Welcome differences of opinion.
m. Develop sensitivity to the emotions children are feeling.
n. Recognize bits of humor, or introduce them when tension needs to be reduced.
o. Make it possible for all to participate.
p. Keep the time for discussion flexible.
q. Give the group experiences on which they can base further discussion.
r. Learn to stop discussion before the children are bored.
s. Involve those who arrive late without stopping what is going on.
t. Seat the children so that they feel free to talk.
u. Ask for, or bring up, many concrete examples.
v. Learn to move further in the direction indicated by the children.

The pamphlet from which these points are taken is a most stimulating one. In it Dr. Lindberg has given carefully thought-out examples in which the teacher can almost see these situations happen.

4. Using the dramatic playing-out of the situation as a way of further understanding:

Especially in the case of the open-ended stories, it is possible to have the children act out the rest of the story and get the feeling of the situation itself. If they go back to the beginning and play the story as far as it was told, it gives them a chance to feel their way into the various parts. Then when the story, as it was told, is finished, many children will go on and finish it without realizing that they are doing so.

When the first ending has been acted out the teacher may then ask those who served as audience to criticize what was done and said and see if the "audience" would not like to become "actors" and supply another and different ending for the situation. It often happens that a child taking a part in such a dramatic situation will furnish an ending that he would never have thought of in the more formal setting of class discussion.

However, the teacher will want to avoid asking the bully to act the role of bully; or the intolerant child to act that role in the hope that this "will make him see the error of his ways." These stories are not intended for such a use, but rather for the spontaneous dramatic continuation which the children volunteer. A safe rule is to allow each child the opportunity to offer to play the part which he wants to play, and *never* to put pressure on a child who does not wish to participate.

This is simple dramatics, the kind the children have often been accustomed to in school when they "act out" the stories in their readers or stories which the teacher has told them. It is a most effective teaching device.

5. Using the "Ideas and Questions for Discussion" at the end of the book for classes which are slow about starting discussion or when the children have overlooked an important issue, to introduce concepts that would normally be a part of the child's experience:

Ideas and questions for discussion for each story in this book have been appended, not with the idea that the teacher will present each of these to the class as soon as the story has been told. Rather, they are ideas and questions which have come up in various situations with actual children, or in discussions of these stories with groups of parents or teachers. They will, it is hoped, give the inexperienced teacher a feeling of confidence that she will have ways of handling the situation if spontaneous discussion does not come from the group. And because they represent the thinking of several persons, it is hoped they may give a variety to the discussion that each single teacher alone would not have been able to achieve.

6. *Using the stories as a starting point, and then working with longer book-length materials dealing with the same kind of issues:*

If this is done, two invaluable sources of bibliographical help will be:

Heaton, M. and Lewis, H. *Reading Ladders for Human Relations*. American Council on Education. This is an invaluable bibliography of books in the areas of

> Patterns of family life
> Community contrasts
> Economic differences
> Differences between generations
> Adjustment to new places and situations
> How it feels to grow up
> Belonging to groups
> Experiences of acceptance and rejection

It also contains rich suggestions for teaching techniques. All church schools should have this in their working library.

Kenworthy, Leonard. *Introducing Children to the World*. New York: Harper and Brothers. A bibliography in areas similar to *Reading Ladders,* including film strips and other materials. Also useful in dealing with the U. N. and foreign countries.

TELLING THE STORIES

While these stories can be used effectively by simply reading them from the book, teachers will find that there is a dramatic quality and a stimulating atmosphere to stories that are *told* which does not develop often when they are *read*. Again, the beginning teacher may hesitate to tell stories, feeling more secure if she can read them with the book before her. To help such teachers achieve the more satisfying experience which so often comes when the story has been told, we have included here a few brief suggestions for storytelling quoted from Mrs. Florence Klaber's pamphlet.[1]

LEARNING THE ART OF STORYTELLING

1. *Becoming acquainted with the story:*

What should the teacher do in general to fit himself to carry on the age-old tradition of the teller of tales? First of all he should read the story to himself, in order to appreciate it and to enjoy it for himself. Then he should read it again and yet again, each time visualizing the incidents more and more vividly as dramatic pictures and happenings. He should note the development of the plot from the introduction of the situation, through the conflict, the suspense, the climax and the solution. He should see them as graphic pictures that he is privileged to portray in words — a work of art just as truly as the painting of a picture by line and color.

2. *Remembering the details of the story:*

There are storytellers who believe it is well to memorize a story verbatim. The author, however, disagrees with this theory. If a story is so memorized, it might almost as well be read aloud.

The best storytellers leave room for something new in each telling. The watchful teacher sees whether he has made his point; whether the group is "with him." He feels free to alter the words, to emphasize a thought, to soft pedal or to increase an emotional effect, according to the response he meets in the faces and in the attention of the group. It is a mistake to memorize a story in such a way that the wording is not flexible or cannot be manipulated to meet the storyteller's need.

[1] Klaber, Florence. *Modern Techniques of Religious Education: A Primer for Teachers.* Revised and enlarged edition, 1958. The American Ethical Union, 2 West 64th Street, New York, N. Y. This section from the pamphlet is quoted with the permission of Mrs. Klaber and the American Ethical Union.

3. Using the voice effectively:

When the story has been thus carefully assimilated, the teacher will plan how to tell it most effectively. The most important tool at his command is the voice. It is like a great organ on which a person may play, using its many pipes and its various stops to produce the effects desired. The teacher will practice modulating the voice, raising it in a crescendo or dropping it to an audible whisper. He will sense when to rush on in a flood of rapidly flowing words and when to give accent by the use of a hush or a pause.

4. Practicing storytelling:

When all the spade work of becoming familiar with the story and planning its best presentation has been done, the teacher should tell the story aloud — as if to the group of children in his class. If he is fortunate enough to have a recording machine, he should record the story, play it back, and listen attentively. Did he make it clear, interesting, bring out the desired point? How can he improve the telling? As he listens to his own voice and hears the words form themselves, he should evaluate them from the point of view of the mental and emotional age of his pupils. Will they understand and enjoy the story? He should tell his tale again and again to this imaginary audience until he himself is satisfied with the rendition.

Then comes the telling of the story to the class. This is the final test! Now creation is renewed, but it is not a solo. The class creates with the storyteller! He must watch and respond to the reactions of the children. They will help him, especially in the timing. If good listeners begin to wriggle, he will think of a way to awaken their interest. Perhaps he has been talking too slowly. Perhaps his voice has been uninterestingly monotonous. Perhaps he is not speaking distinctly: all may not be hearing. If the clock indicates that there is time, he may add relevant and meaningful details that are vivid and perceivable to the senses. Children respond to what they can see, hear, smell, and very especially to what they can taste. Perhaps more can be made of the feelings of the persons in the story as they meet the situations they face.

Each attempt at storytelling should be regarded as an opportunity for learning. After the story hour, the teacher should take time to think over what happened, what he himself did and how the children acted. Our failures sometimes teach us more than our successes. A storyteller should ask himself such questions as these: Why did I get the order of events confused? Why was it that Ann or Bill or Clark were restless? What important parts of the story did I omit or pass over too quickly? Why was this? Was there anything that I did this time which was better than the time before? In what way can I improve my storytelling the next time?

I
Understanding the child who doesn't "fit"

Harriet's Presents

"Hey, Harriet, wait up!"

Adele came running up the street, her lunch box swinging against her legs, and the thermos bottle inside rattling in rhythm. "Where are you going so fast, anyway?" she asked breathlessly.

"I have to stop at Yolanda's Yarn Shop and get some thread for my mother. She's fixing up some handkerchiefs for me to give to Susan for her birthday. You're going to the party, aren't you?" asked Harriet.

"Oh, sure," replied Adele. Her words seemed to hit the air and then fall into heavy silence. Finally she asked, "What color will these be?" She had to say something.

"One will be pink and the other purple," Harriet answered softly.

No further explanation was needed, Adele knew exactly how they would look. Two plain white handkerchiefs with colored crocheted edges, folded in a yellowish white box. Harriet had given her yellow and blue ones on her birthday, and last Christmas she had given Marie red and green ones when she had had a party. Harriet's mother always made Harriet give two handkerchiefs whenever she was invited to a party.

"I guess Susan's having a big party," said Adele.

"Oh, yes, everybody's invited," commented Harriet. "Are you going to wear the dress you had on at your party?"

"If my mother won't get me a new one," answered Adele. "What are you going to wear?"

The question came out before Adele realized it. She knew what Harriet would wear, just as she knew what Harriet would give for a present. Her mother had crocheted her a blue party dress, which she wore over a pink slip. Adele remembered how different Harriet looked from the other girls at the last party when they had all worn ruffled petticoats that made their dresses stand out. Harriet's dress had hung limp, as though it had been caught in the rain.

Adele remembered how she had wished Harriet had worn one of her school dresses, so she would look more like the other girls. Adele really liked Harriet. She wished she could say something to her now, because she could already hear the answer: "I guess I'll wear the blue dress my mother made."

How Adele wished she could buy a doll or a pencil box to give Harriet for Susan's present! Then no one would say anything about Harriet when she walked into Susan's yard wearing her blue dress and carrying the flat white box in her hand.

"I'm going to wear the blue dress my mother made," said Harriet. The words bolted Adele from her thoughts.

"Oh that's nice," she said. "Well, I guess I'd better turn here and go home. My mother says I have to practice the piano a little longer today, because I won't get my practicing done tomorrow if I go to the party."

"Don't forget the arithmetic homework," reminded Harriet. "I'll call you up at seven-thirty to see if our answers check."

"Okay," yelled Adele as she hurried down the street.

As she came closer to her house she saw Marie, Joan and Linda waiting by her gate. "Hi!" she called out to them.

"What color handkerchiefs is Susan going to get?" asked Linda. "We saw you walking to the yarn shop for the thread." The girls all laughed together.

"Maybe Susan will get red, white and blue because it's near Decoration Day," suggested Marie. "Remember, I got red and green at Christmas."

"No, Susan's getting pink and purple," smiled Adele. "But guess what she's going to wear?"

"The blue dress with the pink slip," chorused the girls. For a while they all laughed and joked about it together.

"I guess I have to go in," Adele reminded herself out loud. "I have to practice. I'll see you tomorrow."

"Hi, Mom, I'm home," called Adele as she hung up her sweater.

"Are the girls excited about Susan's party? I saw you all talking together outside," commented her mother.

"Oh, yes." Suddenly Adele felt sort of funny.

"What's the matter? Wasn't Harriet invited?"

"She'll be there," Adele answered slowly.

Adele went up to her room and took out a flat white box from her dresser. She opened it and looked at the two handkerchiefs. She couldn't laugh about it now. She thought about tomorrow and could almost see Harriet in her blue dress. That didn't seem funny anymore either. Harriet would be smiling sweetly as she found a seat near hers at the party.

She and Harriet always sat near each other everywhere. Everyone in the class knew that they were "best friends." Yet this afternoon, when all the girls were making fun of Harriet, she had joined right in. "Well, I had to," she thought, unconsciously defending herself. If she didn't the girls would laugh at her too.

JANET GIVENS

The Outsider

"Arthur, the rain has stopped and the sun is shining. Why don't you stop reading and go play?" Mrs. Johnson opened the window beside Arthur and put her hand on his book.

"M-m," Arthur grunted and went ahead with his reading, burying his head even deeper.

Mrs. Johnson went on dusting. "My the sunshine makes every particle of dust show up. We've had so many gloomy days lately that I'd almost forgotten how the out-of-doors can look," she said, mostly to herself.

Then she turned to Arthur again, and once more pulled the curtain aside. "The boys seem to be gathering on the Perkinses' porch. I see Matt and Lou, and — yes — there's Bert. Why don't you go over too? They'll be doing something interesting before you know it."

"Yeah, in a little while," Arthur mumbled. "I want to finish this book."

"Arthur! Arthur! What is the trouble? You always say that, and then you don't go. I have to force you out of the house, or you would never play with the other boys." Mrs. Johnson stopped. She had spoken more sharply than she meant to. It was clear that she was provoked.

"I know. I know. Can't a fellow have a minute's peace around here? Why don't you leave me alone?" Arthur growled, putting his hands over his forehead to shield his eyes from his mother's view.

"Arthur, I'm simply not going to let you grow up a bookworm. Reading is fine, and I'm glad that you enjoy it so much, but you need friends too. Even your teacher said you spend too much time by yourself. Now close that book and go out at once, right now!" Mrs. Johnson took the book which Arthur reluctantly gave her. He'd been through this before. When his mother took this tone he couldn't put her off any longer.

"I have to get my sweater. It's upstairs."

"Why don't you wear your jacket? It's hanging in the front entrance," said Mrs. Johnson.

Arthur shook his head. "Naw, that's too hot, I'll get my sweater."

"Anything to delay getting outside. I've never seen your equal. Get your sweater then, and come back down at once. Don't start playing up there. This day is too fine to waste it by staying inside."

Arthur went slowly up the steps. He didn't mind going outside. It would be fun to play with Jep, his cocker spaniel. But he didn't want to join the boys.

He could hear them now. A lot of fooling around. They kidded too much. Arthur couldn't tell when they were joking and when they meant it. But the worst was when they went to play. That he couldn't take.

"If we take Arthur on our team," Bert would say, "then you have to give us Joe."

Last week Lou had said, "Now see here, you call this a player?" when Arthur was sent to his side because no one had chosen him. He'd gone on, "Fellows, we have three strikes against us before we start. No thank you, you take him on your side. This is a game, not a side show."

Then there were those awful times when the boys would say,

"Go back to your books, can't you? Why are you always hanging around? What a creep!"

Arthur tried to start to school early so he wouldn't feel like such an outsider as he walked along with them. Sometimes they were pretty decent about things, and he enjoyed being with them. But he never could say the right thing. No matter what he said it turned out to be wrong.

He had learned not to mention anything he had been reading. If he did that, they called him "Egghead." But if he didn't talk, that was wrong too. Someone was sure to say, "What's the matter? Cat got your tongue?"

Usually it was better to walk around the block if he saw them ahead of him. He couldn't walk slowly enough not to catch them, because they fooled around so much.

It was bad getting to school early too. He tried to walk by the playground without looking at any of the other children. Sometimes they didn't notice him. He would peer hard at the sky if an airplane was going over. Sometimes someone would say, "What kind is it, Arthur?" That he liked. He was the best "spotter" in the room, and the kids all knew it.

The best days were those when he could help the teacher before school started. Miss Smith didn't want him every morning. She was like Mom and Dad, and thought he should play with the boys. But it was swell the mornings she needed help. Arthur could walk to school and explain at the door that Miss Smith was expecting him.

"Arthur!" It was his mother calling again. "Why are you dawdling so? Any other time you'd take two steps at once," she called.

Maybe the boys are gone, he thought hopefully as he opened the door. No such luck, there they were, still on the Perkinses' porch. His mother was watching him from the window.

"Oh, well. Here goes," he said to himself. He took a quick breath and went down the front walk.

LUCILE LINDBERG

Replacement for Bill

Jim sat excitedly on his front door steps watching the moving van pull up to the curb next door. This was it! His new neighbors were finally moving in!

Jim remembered the last time he sat watching a moving van trying to park. That was when Bill was moving away. My, how he had hated to see him go. It was just like having a brother when Bill lived next door. They did everything together.

But all during the summer the white house had been empty, except for the painters and electricians and plumbers who would come every once in a while to do something in the house.

Today the new people were finally moving in. Jim knew there was a boy his age, because the new boy's father had talked with Dad early in the summer, just a little while after Bill had left. He had mentioned Stephen and talked about the school he would go to. Stephen was in the fourth grade too.

The moving van was starting to unload now, and Stephen's father was talking to the men. The first piece of furniture to come out was a large, boxlike piece. Jim thought that the moving men must be terribly strong to be able to carry such things on their backs. Soon the men came out of the house and climbed back into the van. They were in there for a long time, but finally Jim saw something edging out of the van. It was very large. As more of it came out, Jim could see that it was a piano. The moving men were having quite a time with it because it was so heavy.

Jim was sure glad that his family didn't own a piano. Goodness knows, they might even make him take lessons! Jim shook his head at the thought of this. Then he began to wonder if Stephen took piano lessons and if he would always have to wait for him to finish practicing before they could play. He hoped not!

After a few more pieces had been unloaded the van pulled away. Jim decided to ride his bicycle. "I hope Stephen has one," thought Jim. "It would be fun like it was with Bill. I didn't see one come out of the van though."

Soon Jim's mother called him for lunch, and he leaned his bike against a tree and went in. He was still thinking about Stephen and wondering what he would be like. "Hope he likes hamburgers with plenty of catsup on them. Boy, it will be fun to have a friend next door again," he thought.

Just as Jim was finishing his last mouthful of cake he heard a rumbling noise and realized the moving van must be back. He quickly put his dishes in the sink and ran outside to watch from the steps. Two men emerged from the front seat followed by a boy.

"That must be Stephen!" exclaimed Jim to himself. Too excited to move, Jim could only sit and watch. He noticed the boy was wearing dungarees like his, only not quite so faded. "Oh, boy," he thought, "just like Bill."

Stephen saw Jim on the steps and started over. Jim got up and went to meet him.

"You must be the boy who lives next door," said Stephen.

"Yeah, you must be Stephen."

"Yup. I'm going to live next to you."

There was silence for a minute. Then Jim asked, "Did your bike get moved yet?"

"I don't have a bicycle," replied Stephen.

"Are you going to get one soon?" Jim went on, too disappointed to stop with the first answer.

"I don't know. I never rode one," admitted Stephen.

"I'll teach you if you get one," Jim said eagerly.

"Do you have any records?" It was Stephen's turn to start asking questions.

"What kind of records?"

"Phonograph records. You know, the kind with orchestras and everything. Which ones do you like?"

"I don't have any. Do you play the piano or something?" Jim was growing more disappointed all the time.

"My mother plays the piano. I play the violin, and my dad plays the cello. We play together. Does your family play together too?"

"Just Chinese checkers," said Jim glumly.

Stephen started to ask all sorts of questions about school, but

Jim couldn't answer them with much enthusiasm. Stephen didn't have a bicycle, and he would have to practice every day. He wasn't like Bill, not at all. Jim wished Bill was moving back instead of Stephen moving in.

During the next week the two boys walked to school together, and Jim showed Stephen around the building. Jim found Stephen wasn't so bad, if only he wouldn't talk so much about music. It sounded as though he didn't mind taking violin lessons.

One morning Stephen burst into the house with exciting news. "My father got some tickets for a concert in New York this Saturday, and he said I can bring you!"

New York! Jim loved to go there. His own parents always took him during a holiday vacation, and they'd eat out and then go into the department stores. Jim couldn't imagine what the concert would be like, but he didn't like to think of sitting still so long — especially if he were in New York!

Stephen continued, "My father says we'll leave in the morning, eat lunch in the Automat — a place where you put your money in slots like a gum machine, and sandwiches and cake and everything come out! Then we'll go to the concert!"

"Yeah?" said Jim, who couldn't see why anyone would want to spoil such a nice day with a concert. "How long does the concert take to be over?"

"I don't know, but we'll be home in time for supper," replied Stephen.

Jim was really stumped. He wanted to go, but he wasn't sure about the concert. Finally he decided that the trip was too good to pass up, so he told Stephen he would go. The rest of the way to school the boys talked about what they'd see, the train ride, and everything else about the trip — that is, everything except the concert.

Saturday morning came, and Jim was up early and dressed in his good suit. Stephen was ready early too, and the boys talked outside until Stephen's father came out. At last they were on their way.

The train ride was good, and lunch in the Automat was even more fun than Jim had imagined. He forgot all about the concert until Stephen's father reminded them. Their seats were to be in the second row in the balcony.

They took a bus to the place where it was to be held and went in with a lot of other people. "How dark!" Jim thought. "Just like the movies." He wished it were the movies.

Soon the concert began. The first piece was played by the full orchestra. Jim thought they made a lot of noise, especially when the drums were so loud. He counted the number of selections on the program and figured it was going to be more than another hour. He hoped perhaps they would skip some of the pieces. But of course they didn't. By the time the last piece came he was squirming. He couldn't remember ever having sat still so long, and he was very glad it was ending. It wasn't worth it, not for all the Automats in the world!

The next day Jim was looking at the funny paper when the phone rang. It was Stephen.

"Can you come over this afternoon?" he wanted to know.

Jim wasn't taking any chances. "What will we do," he asked.

"We are going to play some pieces together," said Stephen.

"Gosh, didn't I have enough of that yesterday?" exclaimed Jim.

"You mean you didn't enjoy the concert!" Stephen couldn't understand how anyone could fail to enjoy that.

"No, the pieces were too long," answered Jim.

Both boys were silent for a while. At last Jim spoke, "Why don't you come over here? We could play checkers."

"I don't like games like that," Stephen said.

"Well, then I guess I'll go catch some fish," sighed Jim.

"Where do you catch fish?" asked Stephen.

"In back of the County Bank. There's a creek."

"Where's that?" asked Stephen.

"Oh, you need a bicycle to get there. You turn by the gas station next to school and ride till you get to the highway. It's only a block from there."

"Do you eat the fish?" Stephen seemed curious.

"No, they're not good eating."

Stephen still questioned, "You mean you catch them just for fun?"

"No, I catch them and keep them in water. The kind that live in my fish tank."

"I've never done that. I think I'd like it. Mind if I come?"

"You can't, you haven't a bicycle."

"Well I can walk fast," said Stephen.

"Okay," answered Jim.

"Now I've done it," he scowled. "I'll have to ride slowly just so he can keep up with me."

Then he turned to his mother and said, "Mom, I'm going to fish."

"Alone?" asked his mother.

"No, Stephen's going with me."

"My, that's nice. I'm glad you have a new friend to take Bill's place."

Jim didn't answer. He wasn't sure yet. Maybe it would work out.

JANET GIVENS

Nature Study

"Wait a minute, I'll get some money from Mom," Slim called as he darted up the front walk and onto the porch.

David, Arthur, and Lee stood waiting.

Then Arthur spotted Peter walking on the sidewalk across the street.

He put his hands up to his mouth and shouted, "Peter, want to go to the movies with us?"

David called over too. "Come on," he urged.

Peter came across the street. "Thanks. Some other time," he said.

Then he added, "I have a chance to go butterfly hunting. Uncle Mark is going to take me with him when he goes out to his farm. The last time we were out there I caught three wonderful specimens. I have to hurry, he doesn't like to wait for me."

Peter walked down the street as Slim opened the front door.

"Listen to this," David said as Slim joined the group. "Peter doesn't want to go to the movies. He's going butterfly hunting."

"So what!" said Slim.

"It's all right for him to hunt butterflies, if he wants to. If only he'd keep it to himself. The thing I don't like is when he brings all his precious things to school."

"He'll bring them, that's for sure! Did you ever know him to skip anything?" Arthur asked.

"Nobody really wants to see them. All the kids are bored," David chimed in.

"Miss Smith will want to see them. If you want to make a hit with her, bring butterflies," Lee added.

"Or toads, or gold fish, or flowers, or leaves! Wasn't it funny last week when he brought in that piece of moss. What were we supposed to do? Clap or something?" David asked. "What's so wonderful about moss, anyway?"

"He's not a bad kid," Lee said. "He's plenty good with a base-ball bat in his hand."

"Sure, but he doesn't have any sense. If he did he wouldn't tell us about all of his exciting experiences hunting violets at the edge of the pond and watching bugs spin on top of the water."

"Agreed," said Arthur. "Who wants to hear that all the time?"

The boys had been walking along toward town. Suddenly Arthur leaned over and picked up a stick. "Look!" he said.

The boys drew close to him.

"Look at what?" Dave asked.

"Can't you see?" Arthur said to him.

"See what?" Dave was really puzzled now.

Arthur laughed. "Can't you see this is a very special stick?"

They all laughed now, because he was imitating Peter.

"I was on my way to the movies when I noticed something long and brown lying on the sidewalk. I picked it up, laid it carefully in my handkerchief, and what do you think it was? It was this stick. If you look at the end you can see that it was broken from a tree. Look carefully and see it is still alive inside. You can tell by ——"

"Yes, and look what I have," Dave cried holding up a green

leaf. "You may think that this is an ordinary leaf, but if you look closely —— "

Slim had gotten into the spirit of the occasion. He found a pebble. "This," he said, "is a pebble which has broken loose from the Joneses' sidewalk."

"Why don't we take all this to school Monday and show it?" Arthur asked.

"What a laugh! I can just hear the kids holler!" Dave exclaimed.

"What about Miss Smith? I don't believe we should," Lee told them.

"I dare you," Slim said. "It would serve Peter right — him always making us do nature study."

LUCILE LINDBERG

No Room for Jerry

Wham! Bill hit the ball full force and it flew high to left field where Jerry was standing with his arms stretched high.

"Get under it," Lane called.

"Run up on it, will you? You sucker!" Perry yelled.

The ball landed on the field several feet from Jerry, and Bill made a home run.

"What do you think? Think they'll come right to you?" Lane shook his head as he spoke.

"Great stuff!" Philip cried. "We need a left fielder, not a statue."

Bob came running. "Get him out of there. We've had enough of this. Lou, you take left field. And Jerry, you get lost. Maybe you can play in the sandbox," he said, casting a knowing look toward the other end of the playground where the kindergartners were.

Jerry threw his glove down, and with head hanging went over and stood by the fence.

"Now send it right here," Harold yelled from his post as catcher as he pounded his glove with his fist. "Burn it up!"

"Play ball!" and they were off.

"Just a minute," called Mr. Martin as he entered the playground. "Let's make room for Jerry."

"Oh, heck, Mr. Martin," Bob complained. "He had his chance. How do you expect us to play ball with that dumb cluck on the field?"

"You know the rules. Everyone has a chance. Come, Jerry, how would you like to play second base? I think there's an empty spot there," Mr. Martin spoke reassuringly as Jerry hesitated and then came out.

"Oh, no! Not there. Not now," Perry pleaded. "Frankie is up to bat, and he always bats them there. Let him play shortstop."

But Frankie was struck out this time. Then Aaron hit one to first and was out, and just then the bell rang.

Lou, and Perry and Harold stopped on the way to the gate.

"Mr. Martin can make us play with him at school, but we don't have to after school. No one can make us." Harold was very emphatic.

"My mom probably will, though. She has the same ideas about giving everyone a chance." Lou scraped the dust back and forth with his toe as he spoke.

"Then we won't play where your mother can see us," Perry said positively. "Let's get a place to play Saturday morning, and then we will only tell the boys we want. The others can play here."

"Good idea! Where will it be?" Perry wanted to know.

"The lot behind Sandy's place. It was empty last Saturday," Harold said after thinking a minute.

"Gee, that's a neat place. It's real flat. We can pull those big weeds at the back." Lou was already beginning to plan.

"Hey, Bob!" they called, and he fell back to walk with them.

"Count me in," he said after he heard the plans. "We don't want that drip, Jerry."

"There's a few others we could do without," Harold added. "Let's make this a super-duper team."

"Meet in my garage after school, and we'll make a list," Bob suggested.

"Righto," they chorused.

"Think you're smart, don't you?" Perry said out of the corner of his mouth as he passed Jerry's seat. "Mr. Martin takes your side. Wait till Saturday and then see where you'll be — one lonesome chicken."

Jerry heard, but he didn't look up.

LUCILE LINDBERG

Three Strikes and Out

"Strike three!" Harry called.

Ronnie threw his bat to the ground in fury, and Joe and Syd jumped out of the way as it hurtled across the hard surface of the playground and hit the fence.

"You-you-you . . . " Ronnie choked out in rage shaking his fists and advancing toward Harry.

Just then Ronnie felt a firm hand on his arm. Mrs. Dennis led him from the playground, although recess was almost over.

At the gate Ronnie pulled away from her, and shook his fist yelling back to the boys, "I'll get even with you! Wait till after school."

Mrs. Dennis held more firmly to his arm, and they walked up the steps into the schoolhouse.

"Who does he think he is?" said Joe.

"It's all right for the rest of us to get strikes called, but he can't take it." Leslie passed the ball from one hand to the other as he spoke.

"That was a strike, clear as anything. What's eating that guy?" Harry wanted to know.

"Sure, it was a strike, but that doesn't make any difference to him. He can't take it, I tell you," Leslie replied.

"Let's quit. I don't feel like playing any more. It's too hot!" said Joe as he picked up the bat. "Let's go and sit in the shade."

"See. It's happened again. We're having a good game. Then that guy comes along and either we end in a fight, or we don't feel like playing any more," Leslie pointed out.

"How long are we going to let this go on?" Harvey asked.

"Yeah, he spoils things wherever he goes. He got put out of the scout troop because he caused a big rumpus every time he came, and the scout master finally got sick of it. That's what we ought to do—put him out." Leslie was insistent.

"How can we do that?" asked Syd. "He's the best player we have. He can hit further than anyone else. We need him."

"Need him! Need him, you say! What for? Suppose he can hit? If he breaks up the game every time, what good does he do us?" asked Leslie.

"I think it would be good to put him out, but how can we?" asked Joe. "If we didn't let him play, he'd get plenty mad."

"Suppose he does?" Harry wanted to know. "So let him."

"Have you ever seen that guy when he's mad? He'd kill us," Joe said.

"Aw, come on. What chance would he have against all of us?" Leslie asked. "You aren't scared of him, are you?"

"Yes, I am," Joe answered. "Say, when that guy gets really mad nothing will stop him. He beat Stuart up the other day."

"Anyway, I don't think we'd better take any chances. He'd lay for us. I don't want to have him jump out at me sometime when I'm all alone," Joe told them.

"Gee, guys like that get by because fellows like you are sissies," Leslie retorted.

"Take that back! You can call me a lot of things and I don't mind, but sissy, never. Take that back!" Joe yelled.

"All right then, you aren't scared. Let's make a plan. Next time he comes around wanting to play, we'll tell him 'no' and if he starts roughing anyone up we'll all jump him. We'll show him he can't get by with this," Leslie was planning with enthusiasm.

"Not let him play with us, ever? I don't think that's very fair. Listen, the guy can't stop himself. He can't help it!" Syd told them.

"He can't help it?" Leslie looked at Syd with disgust. "So I haul off and sock you one, so I can't help it! How do you like that?"

"Difference is you could help it, but that guy really can't," Syd told him.

"Besides, you know what's going to happen. We all gang up

on Ronnie, and Mrs. Smith will be out here in two minutes and we'll all be marched into the office. We'll be staying after school, and that guy will go free."

"You mean we can't do anything with him?" Harry asked.

"Well, what can we do? You figure that one out," Syd said.

"There must be something. We can't go on this way," Harry agreed. "But I don't know what it is."

LUCILE LINDBERG

Mama's Boy

Joe, Pete, Jerry, Oscar, and Haven were standing by Pete's garage when suddenly Joe looked up and said, "Guess who's coming down the street! None other than Fatty McKee in person. Want to have some fun?"

The boys looked up with interest. They didn't have anything exciting planned for the morning. Fatty was in their class at school, but they didn't play with him. Nobody did. Fatty was a pain. He waddled along and whined when he talked.

Joe moved out to the sidewalk and waved and yelled to Fatty who was still a block away. "Hello, hello, Fatty! Some friends want to see you! Come here!"

Fatty broke into a run.

"Look at that run," Jerry laughed. "Look at him."

"What's up? What are we going to do?" Haven asked.

"Wait till he's even with that tree. Then we jump behind these bushes and start peppering him with snowballs. Get it?"

The boys nodded in anticipation. This was going to be great sport. Joe always was able to think of something to do.

"Hi, Fats, where are you going?" Joe called as he came nearer.

"Nowhere special. What are you doing?" Fatty called back.

"You'll soon see!" Joe called. "To your posts, fellows," he said quietly.

They darted behind the bushes, and the snowballs began to fly.

What an expression Fatty had on his face! It seemed too funny for words. He was frightened! This was fun.

The snowballs came fast with five boys to throw them. Fatty turned and ran down the street.

"Watch him run home to mama!" Jerry taunted.

"After him," Joe called.

And down the street they went. Fatty couldn't move very fast, so the boys kept reaching down for more snow. Snowball after snowball hit him. His coat was white with snow.

"Charge," Joe called.

Oscar reached Fatty first and threw him onto a snow bank. "What shall we do with him?" he wanted to know. "Stuff his mouth with snow?"

"Oh that's too good for him," Jerry said, winking broadly at the other boys. "Let's make him up in a snowball, and put a snowman's suit on him. He'll make a fine fat one. We'll roll him up and leave him there. When the snow melts there he will be!"

"Good idea!" Oscar agreed.

"No! Oh, no!" sobbed Fatty. "Please, no! Don't leave me to freeze. Let me go. I'm cold."

"Look at him! Isn't he a pretty sight," Joe said. "Those tears will freeze on his face. Then won't he be beautiful?"

"So you don't want us to make a snowman out of you! And what's to stop us?" Haven kidded.

Fatty shook his head and tried to talk, but he could only blubber and cry.

"Aw, stop that blubbering, or we *will* fill your mouth with snow," Joe told him.

"I know," said Pete. "Let's poke snow down the back of his neck. One time kids did that to me and is it awful!"

Oscar held Fatty's head up, Joe sat on his feet, and the others stuffed snow down his neck.

"Now watch him," said Pete. "Boy when that snow goes falling down his back! Listen to him yell. What's the matter, Fatty?"

Fatty got up and started to run.

"Run home to mama now. She'll dry your clothes by the radiator. What a mama's boy you are," Joe called after him.

"Look at him, look at him," Jerry was bent double laughing. "Funniest thing I ever saw."

"What if he catches cold? We'll be to blame," Haven said.

"He won't catch cold," Oscar answered. "His dear mama won't let him get that far from the radiator."

"She won't let him out of the house for a week," Pete said.

"Right," Joe added.

Pete slapped Joe on the back. "That was a whale of a good time, Joe. I have to hand it to you — you have ideas. I can still see his face when those snowballs started. He didn't know what to think," and he started laughing again.

LUCILE LINDBERG

II
Ethical issues

Ticket to a Football Game

Paul and his father went to the first football game of the season together. It looked as though just about everybody in the town had turned out to watch the game. The stands were filled with crowds, both teams played well, and the home team had won.

"We've got a good team this year," Paul remarked on the way home.

"If they keep this up, they'll be as good as we were when I played," Father said laughing.

"Do you think I'll get on the team when I'm in high school?" Paul asked eagerly.

"I don't see why not," his father said.

They took a shortcut through a neighbor's yard. The fallen leaves crunched under their feet, and Paul felt the cool afternoon air tingle on his cheeks. He was still excited from the football game.

"I'll race you to the house," he called. He dashed across the lawn and reached the kitchen door several feet ahead of his father.

The kitchen was warm and filled with smells that made Paul hungry.

"We're home, Mother," Paul called. "We won!"

Paul described the game to his mother as he nibbled on the freshly baked cookies she had set out for them.

All through the next week Paul practiced football with his best friend, David. They used David's old football until it fell apart. Then Paul bought one of the new ones that had just come in at Randy's Auto Supply store. It took all that week's allowance and all the money Paul had saved, but it was a good bargain just the same!

Friday afternoon David and Paul walked home by way of the high school to watch the team practice.

"It's a home game this week," David said as they were walking home. "Are you going?"

"Sure," Paul answered, absent-mindedly jingling two loose coins in his pocket. He took the two pennies out and looked at them. "At least I'm going if I can persuade my father to give me an advance on my allowance."

He shook his head, "My father is so funny about money. I asked him last night for an advance, but all he said was that I should learn how to plan more carefully. I'll try again tonight."

"Why don't you get a paper route, like mine," David suggested.

Paul shook his head again.

"You're just lazy, that's why," David laughed. He moved out of Paul's reach.

"I'll see you tomorrow," he called as he ran home.

Saturday morning was clear. There had been a frost during the night, and there was a nip in the air. Paul was raking up leaves from the backyard as his father backed the car out.

"Goodbye!" Father called from the car window. Paul put his rake down and ran to the car. He thought he'd try one more time.

"Dad, couldn't I have — — "

"No, I'm sorry you have to miss the game this afternoon, but you must start learning." He waved to Mother and Nancy who had just come outside, and then he left. Paul watched Nancy wade into the leaves he had just raked up.

"Well," he said, "I guess I'll go and see what David is doing. I'll finish the raking this afternoon while David's at the game."

"Have a good time," Mother said cheerfully, and then added, "Oh, Paul, before you come home would you ride around by Reilley's Market for a loaf of bread." She went inside for the money while Paul got his bicycle out of the garage.

The rest of the morning went so quickly that Paul was surprised when David's mother came out to call them in for lunch. "I called your mother," she said to Paul. "She says you may stay and have lunch with us. But she wanted me to remind you to get the bread on the way home."

Paul left David's soon after lunch and started out on his errand. On the way he stopped to talk with two boys who were in his class at school. As they talked they could hear the sound of band music coming from the direction of the high school.

"We're going to be late for the game," said one of them. "Let's go Fred."

"Silly, they're just warming up," Fred answered. He turned to Paul, "Why don't you come with us?"

"I'm not going this afternoon."

"Why not? It's going to be one of the best games of the season!"

"Why not come?"

"No," said Paul shortly, and followed slowly as the boys rode down the street.

The traffic grew heavier as Paul neared Reilley's Market. On both sides of the street groups of people were hurrying toward the high school. The store was across from the entrance to the football field, and after he had propped his bicycle against the building, Paul watched the people. The band began to play again, and he heard the cheers which meant the teams were running out onto the field.

Then suddenly Paul found himself crossing the street and getting near the gate. So many people were going in that he wondered if he couldn't just get by in the crowd without buying a ticket. He stopped and watched a minute longer. He knew he shouldn't do it. A great cheer went up from the grandstand, and Paul finally hurried through the gate as far away from the ticket booth as he could get. He looked around and moved further into the field quickly. He didn't feel happy about it, but at least no one seemed to have seen him!

During the first quarter Paul stood near the wire next to some older boys. They weren't paying any attention to him, but he almost felt as if he were with them. Then he saw some boys he knew sitting on the ground just under the wire. He slipped down beside them.

"Get back of the wire there." The voice behind Paul was familiar, and he looked up to see Mr. Koldinski the policeman who directed traffic by the school. Paul jumped up and tried to smile at Mr. Koldinski whom he had known ever since he went to kindergarten. But he didn't feel as friendly as usual, and after saying "Hello," he turned and pretended to be very interested in the game.

"Quite a game this afternoon, isn't it?" Mr. Koldinski boomed cheerfully. Paul just nodded. "Well, be good," said the policeman, walking away. Paul looked after him, wondering if Mr. Koldinski had seen him sneak by the booth. He didn't feel very happy.

The game seemed very long, and it wasn't as much fun without Father explaining things to him. But finally it was over, and Paul got the bread and his bicycle and started home. He took the long way home so it was almost dark when he turned into his driveway. Finally he went into the house.

Mother was in the kitchen. He put the loaf of bread down on the table.

"Paul!" Mother sounded cross. "Where were you all afternoon?"

Just then Father came out. "Paul you are very late. What have you been doing all afternoon?"

"Nothing much," Paul began. "I had lunch at David's, and then — — " Suddenly he wanted to tell his father about the football game.

"Then I went to the game. It was good. You should have seen Jones kick, and Kelly made two touchdowns, and, and — it was a good game." He wished his father would stop looking at him.

"Where did you get money for a ticket?" his father asked.

"I — — I sneaked through the gate. Nobody saw. Most of the kids do it, every week."

"They do?"

"Well, some of them. Anyway, what's the difference? They don't really care." Paul was feeling a little more uncomfortable as he tried to explain.

"I think you do know why it makes a difference," Father said.

"I guess I know," Paul agreed, "but there were hundreds of people there. My quarter wouldn't have made much difference. It wasn't as though I were stealing." Paul began to speak very loudly. Then he asked anxiously, "Are you going to punish me?"

"Suppose you tell me just how you feel about this afternoon," Father said, not answering the question at all.

Paul thought about the afternoon. He wasn't sure he could tell how he felt. It was a funny thing for his father to ask, but here was Father waiting as though Paul's answer would be very important.

ESTHER BAILEY

The Dream Camp

Nancy squirmed and wished something would happen. That the phone would ring or someone would come to the door, anything. Just so she wouldn't have to discuss this with Mother.

She should have remembered that Susan told her mother everything. Then of course Susan's mother *would* tell Mother. What a mess!

Nancy didn't know why she had done it. It had just come tumbling out. All of the girls were talking so big about the camps they were going to this summer. When they asked her where she was going she couldn't bear to say that she wasn't. They would know it was because her folks couldn't afford it. So she had made up a camp right on the spot, Camp Joyce, in the Michigan woods. She had put it far enough away so that no one would know about it. Then she had described the lake with perfect swimming, the ponies and horses for riding, hikes, and even the dining hall.

Nancy had never been to camp, but it was easy to describe one. She simply elaborated on what the others had said, and the girls were impressed because her dream camp had everything. The girls need never have known that this wasn't true, if only mother hadn't — — Oh well, now it had happened and it was dreadful.

"Nancy, why did you do it?" Mother continued. "I thought at first they had misunderstood you, until they began describing the camp and even the name of it. Nancy, how could you? Why didn't you tell them you were going to Grandma Roth's for the summer?"

Nancy was uncomfortable, but she didn't feel like talking about it. She didn't want to think about it again, ever.

"I know you don't wish to discuss it," Mother said, "but we do need to talk. You tell stories like this all the time. Why do you do it?"

"Oh, Mother, it's so horrid. All of the girls are going away to camp. I'm the only one who isn't. I can't have them know I'm not going. What will they think when they find out I'm just going to Grandmother's this summer? It's awful."

"But, Nancy, what would the girls think? Wouldn't they be pleased to know that you are going to have such a good time? You always have fun there."

Nancy's tears ran still faster, and Mother handed her a tissue. Why couldn't Mother see how dreadful this was? She didn't seem to understand that to be the only one not going to camp made her feel like an outcast. All of the other girls had something to talk about, and Nancy felt like a fool because she had nothing to add.

"What would the girls think?" Mother insisted.

"They would know we are poor. It's terrible not having things. The other girls have everything they want, and we can never have anything," Nancy sobbed.

"We aren't any poorer than the other girls. Whatever made you think we were?" asked Mother.

Nancy was very upset. "The other girls have more clothes than I have, and the Joneses have a new car, and Carol had a party, and they all go to camp, and just everything," said Nancy.

"It's true we haven't been able to do some of the things we would like to do the last couple of years, because we had to pay for my operation, and Billy had his tonsils out. Daddy has been putting a little money each year into his company, but that is really saving, and we expect it to help put you children through college one of these days. That doesn't mean we are poor!"

Nancy was beginning to feel ashamed, and yet she was still angry too. "I don't see why we must be so practical in this family," she moaned. "Why can't Daddy let us charge things like the other girls do?"

"I've often felt that way myself," said Mother. "But when the end of the month comes bills have to be paid. All of your friends don't have new cars. The Smiths bought theirs the year before we did, and the Pattersons have two cars, and Rita Peyton's family doesn't have any. Each family spends its money in a different way."

"I don't like to be the only one not going to camp," Nancy said rather feebly.

"I'm sure you don't. I'm sorry you can't go this year since you want to so much, but we can't manage it. Maybe next year we can send you."

Nancy was still feeling miserable. She couldn't bear to face what Sue and all the others would think when they found out that she had made up the whole story.

"I can't ever go with the girls again," she sobbed. "Never, never, never! What will they think of me?"

LUCILE LINDBERG

Why Janie Cheated

Helen banged the door and threw her books down on the table. Mother turned around and started to dry her soapy hands. "Goodness, what a racket! Whatever is the matter?" she asked.

"It just isn't fair," Helen said.

"What isn't?"

"Janie's cheating. We had another science test today."

"And?" said Mother.

"Well, Janie got a hundred. That's all." Helen looked at Mother and continued.

"This time she got Nancy to give her the answers. Nancy had the same test this morning, so she told Jane the answers, and Jane memorized them during lunch. We all saw her."

"Did anyone say anything?" asked Mother.

"No. Betsy memorized them too, but the rest of us just sat there. We don't think Mr. Green gives fair tests. They are too hard."

"What do you mean?"

"Well, if Janie didn't always get a hundred, then Mr. Green would see that his tests are too hard. Today some of the questions were from a part of the book we haven't studied yet. But if we say anything, he says, 'If Jane can answer the questions correctly, I don't see why the rest of you can't.' What are we supposed to do? We don't want to tell on her. I hate tattlers."

"Maybe you could say something to Jane," Mother suggested. "You are certainly together often enough."

"I know," sighed Helen. "We're supposed to meet over at her

house in a few minutes to listen to her new records. Maybe I'll get courage enough to say something."

Helen went to her room and in a few minutes came back wearing her blue jeans and flannel shirt.

"Don't you want a glass of milk?" asked her mother.

"Oh, no. Jane always has lots of cokes. It's nice at her house." Helen put on her coat and opened the door.

"Don't spoil your supper with too much sweet stuff," reminded Mother.

As Helen walked along she practiced what she would say to Jane. She even hurried a little so that she would be the first one there and could talk with Jane alone.

But the other girls had already come, for Helen heard music coming from the basement. She walked down the steps and entered. Sarah and Margo were dancing together, and Betsy and Nancy were sitting on the floor looking at records. "It will be hard to talk to her now," thought Helen. "I'll have to wait."

They all had a coke and danced for a while. Then Jane's mother came down and took clothes out of the dryer. She stood watching the girls a moment. She looked as though she had something to say.

Jane stopped the record, "Are we making too much noise?" she asked.

"Oh, no," said her mother. "I just thought you'd like to hear the good news. Agnes made the honor roll at high school." Mother laughed and said to Janie, "You'll have to keep getting hundreds like you did in the science test today if you are going to keep up with your big sister."

When she had left it was very quiet in the room. Jane looked as though she wanted to cry. Finally she burst out, "I'm so sick of it! It's Agnes this and Agnes that! Agnes did this, and Agnes got that award. Always Agnes, Agnes, Agnes. I wish I didn't have a sister. Then I wouldn't have to get those old hundreds!" She was sobbing.

No one moved for a few minutes. Then Margo put on her coat. "I've got to help Mother set the table," she said.

"Me too," said Nancy.

"Gosh, I'd better too," Helen said. Jane stopped sobbing, but she seemed relieved that the girls were going. She didn't want to talk to anyone just now. She knew they all knew how she got those hundreds.

As the girls started down the block Betsy said, "I sure do feel sorry for Jane."

"Me too," said Nancy. "No wonder she has to cheat! Still, we've got to help her stop. It isn't fair to anyone when she gets her grades that way."

JANET GIVENS

Making the Test Easier

"All right, class, you may close your books."

Mrs. Tompkins put her book down on the desk and walked over to the big map of the United States that hung on the wall.

"We've just completed our study of the last group of states. You remember we started here in the northeast, and then went southeast, and then over into the middle part of the map, and finally way over here." She pointed to the different sections of the country as she spoke. "Tomorrow there will be a test on all the states. It won't be hard. I just want to see if you can name the states in each of the groups."

A loud murmur swept over the classroom, hushed only by the sound of the closing bell.

"Boy! How do you like that," said Robert. "I hate tests. I don't think I'll come tomorrow. I feel sick already."

"Oh, it won't be too bad," John responded. "I think I could do it now."

"Well, your family is always traveling around on vacations. You've been to most of the states," said Ralph. "But how would I know whether Oregon or Tennessee is next to the Pacific Ocean? I don't like social studies anyway."

"Me either," chorused several of the boys.

"Look at me," Mike groaned. "I had my tonsils out when we

were studying the northeast states, and I had the flu while we were doing the middle western states. I'm going to fail for sure."

"Not if you study tonight," said John.

Bill suddenly shouted, "Say, I've got an idea."

The boys all stopped talking and grouped themselves around Bill. "Let's divide up into groups. Each one of us will learn just part of the material, and those that sit by each other can copy from the guys that are near to him."

"Gee that would make it easy," Robert said. "I could never learn them all, but I could learn part of them." Then he laughed, "Learn part of them, copy part of them — that sure will make the test easier."

"Sure," said Bill, "We can all get a hundred."

"I don't have to do that to get a hundred. I know them already," John said. "Besides, Mrs. Tompkins just wants to know if we know them or not. It wouldn't be fair to learn just a few and let her think you know them all."

"Okay, goody-goody," said Bill.

The other boys walked ahead, slowly. "You know, that would have been good. Leave it to John to spoil it just because he is the one who knows the answers already!"

"I suppose he is right," Robert said grudgingly. "It *is* lying to Mrs. Tompkins. I don't think I really want to do it that way after all."

"Yes, but it means getting a good mark in social studies on our report cards," reminded Bill. "Gee, I'd like that!"

"I know," said Mike.

"Aw come on, John. Be a sport," wheedled Mike, turning back to John again. "Help us guys out, won't you?"

"I'm sorry," John answered, "My dad says helping someone else to cheat is as bad as cheating yourself. I don't like it."

"All right, all right," chorused the other boys. "Go on home John, and start polishing your wings. We can play. *We* don't have any wings to polish."

JANET GIVENS

What Difference Does It Make?

Nancy felt a tug on her collar. Miss Kane was pronouncing the words for the spelling test, so Nancy simply shrugged her shoulders and kept her eyes to the front. Then she felt a more persistent pulling at her collar and a pencil poking her.

"What does Marie want?" she wondered.

Marie was Nancy's very best friend and sat directly behind her. They always had fun together after school. But this wasn't the time for fun. Nancy had a good record in spelling. In fact, she had had all of her words correct every Friday and she was trying to write each of these words with care.

She did wonder what Marie wanted. Perhaps it was something important. So she shifted to one side of her seat and moved her head ever so slightly. After a quick glance to be sure Mrs. Kane wasn't looking, she moved her eyes so she could see Marie.

Marie motioned with her hand for Nancy to move over a little more. Just then Nancy realized what Marie wanted! She turned quickly back to her work, sat up very straight, and placed her hand over her spelling paper.

Marie was trying to look at her paper! Nancy couldn't believe it! She knew some kids cheated, but she didn't expect Marie to do it — not Marie, her very best friend!

Just then Nancy noticed that Miss Kane was walking toward her. Had she seen? "Nancy," Miss Kane said, "what's the matter? Your face is flushed."

"Nothing," she said. "Nothing. It does seem hot in here, but I'm all right."

After the test was over Nancy couldn't keep her mind on her reading. She sat and looked out into space. When the class was dismissed she grabbed her coat and hat and was the first one out of the door.

Marie called after her. "Where are you going so fast? Wait for me!"

Nancy pretended not to hear and walked as fast as she could.

"Wait! Wait!" Marie called, and Nancy could hear her footsteps coming closer. There was nothing to do but wait.

"Why did you hurry off?" Marie said. "I want you to stop at my house and see my new bike. Maybe if you telephone your mother she will let you stay for dinner."

Then she looked at Nancy. "Is something wrong?" she asked. "You're acting so strange."

"Marie, how could you do it!" Nancy blurted out. "Why did you do it?"

"Do what?" said Marie.

Now Nancy was really mad. "You know what! You know very well what is wrong! Why did you look at my spelling paper?"

"Oh that? What's so wrong about that. Everybody copies sometimes. What's eating you?"

"But, it's cheating," Nancy said.

"For goodness sake, is that it? What difference does it make? I told you already, everyone copies. Joe didn't make a big fuss when I copied from his arithmetic paper. What's a few words?"

"Marie, you didn't!" Nancy said. "That isn't fair. Everyone should do his own work."

But Marie went right on. "I had to get all of my words right today. Daddy said he'd give me a dollar if I did."

"Marie, you shouldn't cheat!" Nancy was very earnest. "You're cheating twice, first at school and then your father. I think it's terrible."

Marie had had enough of this. "All right," she said, "if that's the way you feel, cover up your paper so I can't see. I don't care, I have lots of other friends. They're willing to help me."

LUCILE LINDBERG

You Took It

"May I go to the washroom, Miss Farthing? I left my ring on the sink."

"Certainly."

Agnes was back in a few minutes, out of breath. "It's not there, it's gone. Someone has taken it," she said, brushing away a tear.

"Are you sure it has been taken? Perhaps it has been turned in at the Lost and Found. Why don't you go ask?" suggested Miss Farthing.

"I did, but Miss Shirley says that no one has brought in a ring. Someone had to take it. Whoever went in after I did stole it."

"Are you sure it didn't get pushed off onto the floor or down the drain?" Miss Farthing asked.

"I looked. The holes in the drain are too small, and it isn't on the floor. Someone had to take it," Agnes insisted.

"Why don't you go to your seat now," Miss Farthing told her. "Perhaps it hasn't been turned in yet."

Agnes started toward the back of the room. Harriet whispered to her as she went by, "Joy went to the washroom right after you did. She probably has it."

"She's always poking around. I'll bet she has it all right," whispered Lynne in the next seat. Somehow none of the girls liked Joy. She lived in an old house down by the river and just never had seemed to fit in.

"Agnes! Go to your seat at once! It is time to put our things away for recess. Let's clear the tops of our desks," Miss Farthing warned.

The class walked down the hall and out onto the playground.

Harriet turned to Joy. "Why don't you give Agnes her ring? We know you have it."

Joy turned pale and her voice trembled. "I don't have it," she said. "I don't even know what kind of ring it is."

"Give it to her," snarled David. "Why are you trembling if you don't have it?"

"I can't. I don't have it," Joy insisted.

"Yeah, who says so?" Dave continued.

"Let's search her. We'll find it." Ralph started toward her as he said it.

Joy ran across the schoolyard with the boys after her, then she turned and went as fast as she could toward the schoolhouse.

"Joy is a thief! Joy is a thief!" the girls chanted.

She darted into the hall. The boys stopped at the door.

"What are you doing in the hall, Joy? We stay on the playground until the bell rings," Miss Farthing called.

"I can't go out. They say I took Agnes' ring," Joy blurted out. "The boys want to search me."

"Did you?" asked Miss Farthing.

"No. I haven't even seen her old ring," said Joy.

"Then tell them you don't have it, Joy," said Miss Farthing.

"I did, and that's when the boys said they would search me. I can't go out again," pleaded Joy.

"Go to the room then, and we'll talk about it when they come in."

The boys and girls came in angry.

"What's the trouble?" asked Miss Farthing. "You seem upset."

Everyone talked at once. "Joy has Agnes' ring. She went to the washroom after Agnes did, so she has to have it. Where else could it be?" they asked.

"One at a time! Let's calm down and talk about this," insisted Miss Farthing. "There are lots of places it could be. Joy says she doesn't have it."

"Easy to say. Let her prove it," Carl flashed back.

"She says she doesn't have it. Isn't that enough?" Miss Farthing spoke very firmly. "Take out your spelling pads, and we'll continue our work."

It wasn't long after that that the janitor appeared at the door. "Did one of your girls lose this?" he asked. "I found it in the trash basket when I was emptying the paper towels."

Agnes hurried to look at it. "That's mine," she said, putting it on her finger. "It must have gotten into the basket when I dried my hands."

"I just happened to see it," the janitor said. "You are a very lucky girl."

"If you hadn't seen it, I would never have gotten my ring back," said Agnes. "Thank you."

Agnes hesitated and looked at Joy. She should say something. All the children were looking at Joy, but she had her head down on the desk.

LUCILE LINDBERG

The Blue Soldier

Jay stood looking at the toys on the counter in the dime store. His allowance for the week was gone, so he couldn't buy anything. But he liked to look at them anyway.

"Don't touch the toys!" the clerk spoke sharply to him as she went by.

Jay put his hands in his pockets and continued to look. He saw some blue soldiers exactly like those in his set at home. The clerk was busy with people at another counter. Almost without thinking Jay drew one of the soldiers over the edge and slowly pulled it along and down into his coat pocket.

He walked to the door expecting the clerk to call him at any minute, but she didn't, and soon he was outside. Then he walked very rapidly over to the other side of the street.

"What's your hurry?" Lou and Sam ran to catch up to him.

"No hurry, just walking," Jay said.

"Slow up," Lou told him. "We're going your way. Let's turn here and go by Jake's. I want to buy some bubble gum."

The three of them rounded the corner talking as they went. Jay looked ahead and saw two policemen. "Are they waiting for me?" he wondered.

He didn't see how they could know he had taken the soldier, but maybe the man standing by the door as Jay went out had seen him take it. Maybe he had called the police.

"Let's not go this way," Jay said. "I'd rather go on Fourteenth Street."

"You crazy or something?" Sam asked him. "We're going by Jake's, remember? We can go on Fourteenth Street after that if you want to."

They were getting so close to the policemen now that it would look funny to turn back, so he went on with the boys. The policemen didn't notice them at all, and he breathed a sigh of relief.

Lou bought his bubble gum, and the boys walked toward Fourteenth Street. Ahead of them Jay saw a police car!

"Why don't we turn up Thirteenth Street?" he said.

"Make up your mind! Do you know what you want?" Sam asked him.

"Are you afraid of someone?" Lou asked. "Who are you running away from?"

"I'm not running," Jay protested.

"Oh, aren't you?" Sam said. "You've been five steps ahead of us all the time."

Suddenly Jay said, "Oh, I forgot something. I've got to go back to the store." He was off like a flash of lightning. As he approached the dime store he went more slowly. If he returned the soldier to the counter where he got it, he wouldn't feel as though people were watching him.

There weren't many people in the store now, and the clerk was standing by the soldiers talking to the man Jay had seen before. Jay circled around and stood on the other side of the counter hoping they would move away.

The man looked up at him. "Can I help you?" he said.

"That's the boy that stood there so long looking at things," the clerk said. "I thought he had gone."

The man came over. "Look, if you don't want to buy anything, why don't you go home? Children just standing around block the aisles. Come on now, do you want to buy something or not?"

Jay ran out of the store. He had tried to put the soldier back, but he couldn't. Now he would have to keep it. But what would his mother say? She knew he had only eight, and if she saw another one she would ask where he had gotten it. He could tell her he found it. She wouldn't know he had stolen it.

He walked down the alley toward his house. As he passed the Lewis' ash can he had an idea. He slipped the soldier into it. Then he ran home as fast as he could.

LUCILE LINDBERG

Price of Admission

The boys stepped back and admired their work. "Come here," called Joe, who had run out to the sidewalk.

"What is it?" Ray wanted to know.

"Come, and I'll show you. All of you come!" Joe said.

Ray, Pete, Sam, and Pim gave a dozen hop-jumps and were with him.

"See what I see?" Joe asked.

"What?"

"That's what I mean. If you didn't know it was there you couldn't see it at all, now could you?"

The boys looked hard. Pim took five steps to the left and looked. "You can't see it from here either," he reported.

Ray walked a few steps to the right. "It doesn't show from here."

Joe grinned. "It's in plain sight," he said, "and yet no one would ever guess it was there. Perfect for a clubhouse."

Ray started back toward the pile of junk where they had been working all afternoon. They had arranged two car fenders, an old mattress, some wheels, and a piano box so that when they crawled in the entry way there was an empty space big enough to hold all of them. It was almost high enough to stand up, but not quite.

"Hey, where you going? Stop!" Joe said impatiently.

"Let's go inside and talk there," said Ray.

"Yes, let's," said Joe. "But if we aren't careful we will spoil everything. If all of us go walking into that clubhouse, every kid in the neighborhood will know about it. Come here, guys, let's plan."

They crouched together on the curbing. This was interesting!

"This is the idea! We can't act like we are going there. We have to pretend that we are wandering by. Then when we get opposite that pile of junk we look all ways to be sure no one is looking. Then we fall to the ground and go in on our stomachs."

"Let's have a rule that only one person at a time can go in. If two of us are together we separate, and one goes walking that way and the other comes in from the other side, but not at the same time. You understand, don't you? Not at the same time!" said Sam.

"Anyone who doesn't follow the rules is out of the club," added Ray.

"All right, guys, let's practice. Scatter. Sam you be the first to go in. Then when you see that he is in, you are next, Ray. Then Pim, then Pete, and then I'll come in." Joe spoke in a hushed tone.

Ten minutes later they were all in the clubhouse.

"This is great," said Pete. "We can see everything, and no one can see us."

"This is a place to hide when we don't want our folks to know where we are," Pim told them.

"That's something else we'd better talk about. If anyone calls you, you can't go running out. You have to sneak out, and make believe you are coming from somewhere else. If anyone ever knows this place is here, it's all spoiled!" Joe was very insistent.

Ray threw himself down. "Now we have a clubhouse we should get a name for our club," he said.

"And we shouldn't tell anyone the name, just the initials. We'll never tell anyone what they stand for," Pete added.

"And we ought to have some rules. There should be an initiation or something. It should be hard. That's what they do at the college my brother goes to. They initiate their members. They make them do all kinds of things." Joe's face lighted up, and he went on talking. "I know what we could do. Everyone who belongs has to get something from the store!"

"I haven't any money," Pete protested.

"Money!" Joe looked at him in disgust. "Of course not. That's the idea. You take it without paying. It's easy! I've done it lots of times. I almost got caught once."

Pete was scared. "But that's stealing. I don't want to steal."

"Aw, come on. You in on this club or aren't you?" Pim was looking at him.

"I'm in," Pete said weakly.

"And another thing. It doesn't count if one of us guys doesn't see you take it. No one's going to cheat on us and buy his stuff," Pim went on, looking at Pete. "We'll divide up, two of us to the corner store, and three to the five-and-ten. Be back in thirty minutes."

Pim left first. A few minutes later Ray left, and one by one the others followed. Pete was the last one. This was exciting business, and Pete didn't want to be left out. He felt breathless and forced a grin as he met Joe at the corner. He mustn't let the boys know how he felt about this stealing business. They'd always thought he was a baby. Now he could be as grown up as they.

Thirty minutes later they were back. Joe was the last one in. "No one got caught," he said. "Good. We wouldn't want to get caught the first time. I got this little flashlight — perfect for dark nights. What did you get?"

Sam had a ballpoint pen, Ray a pencil sharpener with a dog's head on it. Pim showed a whistle. Then they looked at Pete. He pulled up his sweater and slid out a comic book.

Joe slapped him on the back and beamed at him. "Fine, Pete! I didn't know you had it in you."

Pete's chest swelled a little. He was really one of the gang. He had proved that he did belong!

It was beginning to get dark.

"Let's pick out our name tomorrow," Sam said. "We can think about it."

Pete's feet dragged as he walked home, and he went more slowly with each step. He had made a place for himself with the gang, but he didn't feel very good about it. He couldn't get it out of his mind. He was a thief, yet he had to be one to stay with the gang. Maybe they would want to steal some more!

He opened the kitchen door and slipped off his sweater. He wished he could forget about it all.

LUCILE LINDBERG

III
Social relations involving decisions

The Unhappy Party

"All right, Ray. Come out! We give up," Edith called from the foot of the stairs.

Ray swelled with pride. No one had been able to find him. He jumped out quickly from behind the draperies in which he had wound himself and stayed so flat against the wall that no one had known he was there.

R-r-r-r, came a tearing sound. In his haste he had stepped on the curtain and torn part of it loose. He struggled to get free, and there was the sound of more tearing.

Lon and Fred stepped forward to help, for Ray was really tangled now. Lon took hold of the curtain and gave a big pull. "Now you can get loose," he said, and then he kept on tearing. "Look at me," he cried. "I'm a bandit."

He had taken the piece of curtain and wrapped it around his head.

Fred grabbed at the ragged end of the curtain and pulled for a piece. The whole rod came down, and Fred fell over with it.

The children laughed as Fred struggled to get up. When he heard them laugh he pretended it was harder than it was and rolled over and over, kicking and screaming, and yelling, "Help me! Help me!"

Edith and Sue stepped forward and tried to pick him up by hanging onto the curtain. Evan grasped it and helped. And soon they were swinging him back and forth.

Just then Mildred came to the door. It was her birthday party, and she had been helping put the cake on the table and cut the ice cream. The noise had brought her to the room.

"Stop it! Stop it this minute!" she cried, stamping her foot.

Just then Mildred's mother came to the door too. She gave one quick look at the situation.

"Stop!" she said firmly.

The room became quiet. The children looked surprised. Edith

dropped her end of the drape and began to move back against the wall, hanging her head.

Lou scrambled to his feet. But he began to laugh again. "Look at it!" he howled. "Look at it!"

He lunged at the other curtain and gave it a hard tug so that it came down too. Laughing harder than ever the children all started shouting again.

"Stop! Everybody stop!" Mildred's mother sounded angry now. "You are acting like savages. Get out, all of you! I won't have you stay in this house. What is wrong with you? You can all go right home."

Mildred's mother opened the door and one by one the children stepped out onto the porch. There was a dead silence, broken only by the sound of footsteps.

David broke the silence. He looked up, then down at his feet. "I'm sorry, Mrs. Smith," he said. "I don't know what gets into us. We've been getting wilder and wilder at every party. I'm sorry about the curtains."

"I am too," said Edith.

"And me," chimed in Sue.

"Can't we help fix things up?" Ray asked. "I — — I guess I'm to blame. If I hadn't hidden in the curtains this never would have happened."

"We're all to blame," David said. "We all laughed. We really knew it wasn't funny."

Tears rolled down Edith's cheeks, "I wish I hadn't come. This happens, and I do it, too, and then I'm sorry — — "

The whole group looked glum, and they just stood there. Mrs. Smith didn't say anything for awhile. She seemed to be thinking.

"We all feel badly about it," she said finally. "I feel badly about my curtains because they are ruined. But you feel badly because you didn't really think before you did it. You can come back in, and we'll clean up all the mess.

Fred's face turned red. "You mean you'll trust us again? After what we have done?"

"I don't think you'll forget again today," Mrs. Smith said. "Maybe you have learned enough so this will not happen at another party. Clean it up quickly, and perhaps the ice cream won't be all melted."

LUCILE LINDBERG

Which to Do?

Diane could hardly believe her ears. Mr. Wilson had given her a solo part in the cantata! Every year since she could remember there had been a Spring Festival in the church. Every year the Festival had been exciting, but no year would be more wonderful than this. For Diane was not only going to sing in the cantata for the first time, but she was going to have a solo part!

She ran down the auditorium aisle and hurried into the downstairs room. The other members of the junior choir had left as soon as the practice was over, but Diane had stayed to go over her part again with Mr. Wilson. She hurried into her coat and pulled on her boots. She got outside just in time to see her mother and father disappear into the church.

Diane turned then and walked home. Her younger brother was watching from the door to the living room as Diane took off her boots.

"Hi," said John and sniffed. "Will you play chess with me?" John had had to stay home that morning because he had a cold. His voice was hoarse, and his eyes were red.

"No, you always win. And anyway keep away from me please, I don't want to catch your cold." Diane paused, then added, "A singer has to be careful of her throat."

John made a strange sounding noise and flopped down on the couch. "Whoever thought you could sing!" he exclaimed. Diane ignored him and walked over to the piano, picking out a tune with one finger and humming it softly to herself.

When Mother and Father finally came home from church Diane didn't wait for them to get inside the door.

"Guess what! Mr. Wilson wants me to sing a solo in the cantata for the Spring Festival," she announced. She watched the surprised and pleased looks come to her parents' faces.

"Why that's wonderful, Diane," her mother said. John coughed from the couch, and Mother went over and felt his forehead. He wriggled and sat up.

"Can I go outside this afternoon? David says the snow is melting so fast we won't have many more chances to slide."

Father laughed, "Don't worry son, we'll have more snow before the week is over. The weather doesn't pay attention to an early Easter." He sat down and picked up the newspaper.

Diane followed her mother into the kitchen.

"We will have to practice like mad, Mr. Wilson says. The Festival is just two weeks away, and you know what he told us? He won't let anyone who has missed more than one practice sing in the cantata, and we all have to be at the last practice. Anyone who isn't there that Saturday can't sing the next day. He's terribly strict — I like him though." Diane took a piece of celery from the salad tray her mother was arranging and crunched into it.

"I'm not going to miss a single practice, that's one sure thing. Joan is singing too. Everybody from the sixth grade up can sing in the cantata if he wants to."

Diane followed her mother into the dining room carrying some dishes. "Do you think I could have a new dress?"

"We'll see," Mother said. Then she called to the family that dinner was ready.

The next day Diane and Joan went to choir practice together, and when it was over hurried to the Community Center for their troop meeting. Diane and Joan did almost everything together. They lived on the same street, went to the same church and school. They swam on the same team at the Recreation Center, and just that fall they had joined the Girl Scouts together. They thought their troop had the best times of any in the city.

Usually Diane and Joan were among the first to arrive, but this time the meeting had already begun. The members were in the middle of a lively discussion. Diane and Joan sat down in the two empty seats and listened for a while.

"What's all this about 'sap'?" Joan broke in, trying to make herself heard above the others. The girls laughed, and then they were quiet while Mrs. Colby, the leader, explained what was happening.

"You remember the plans we made last fall to visit a sugar farm, don't you?" she began. "Well, I had a letter from my friend who owns a farm, and the sap has just started to run. It should continue for about three weeks. Now we are trying to decide on a time to make the trip. We have to plan on staying over one night, and — — "

"There was another letter," one of the girls interrupted eagerly. "It was from a Girl Scout troop in the town near the farm. They heard about our wanting to visit, and they are planning to have a sugaring-off party while we are there."

The chatter started again. This time Diane and Joan were talking as loudly as the rest. Each member was responsible for part of the plans. Joan volunteered to find out about the train — how often it ran and what time it went. Diane was to keep a record of the whole trip for the troop notebook: their plans before they went, and what happened during their stay, and then write it up for the local paper when they got back.

"I want to know as soon as you have talked it over with your parents how many of you are going," Mrs. Colby reminded them as they were about to leave.

"Everything exciting seems to happen all at once," Diane said as they were walking home.

"Yes," Joan answered. "Did you know what a sugaring-off party was? I didn't dare ask because everybody else seemed to know. I was glad when Susan asked. Isn't this going to be the greatest fun we have had?"

Snow had begun to fall in large soft flakes. Diane reached out to catch one on her mitten. "I'm so excited I feel like a snowflake," she said.

"You're so silly, Diane. How can you feel like a snowflake? I'm glad it's snowing, though. You need lots of snow for a sugaring-off party."

"You're so clever, Joan," Diane teased, and ran shrieking as Joan went after her with a handful of snow.

At home Mother and Father were as pleased as Diane when

she told them about the trip.

"Everything happens to Diane," John said enviously. "Can I go too? I've never been on a train, and I've never seen maple syrup being made. Couldn't I go?"

"This is just our troop," Diane answered. "We worked hard to earn the money, didn't we?" Mother had been a cookie mother, and she nodded.

"Yes, and we've had to eat your cookies until they just about made us sick," John said.

"When will you go?" Father asked.

"As soon after school on Friday afternoon as we can. It depends on when the train leaves. That's two weeks from next Friday, and — — " Suddenly Diane put her hand to her mouth. Her eyes grew large, and at the same time Mother stopped smiling.

"What's the matter with you two?" Father asked curiously.

"Ohhh," Diane groaned, "the cantata! How could I have forgotten? That's the same week end as the Spring Festival."

"Will you be gone Sunday too?"

"No, but we won't be back till Saturday night. I'll miss the last practice." An idea came to her.

"Mother, maybe if you asked Mr. Wilson, and told him how I already know my solo part — — "

"No, I can't ask for you. You might go to him after your practice and ask him. But he has made the rule, you know."

That was one of the longest weeks Diane could remember. She was tired of going to choir practice twice in the same week. She stayed behind after the Saturday morning practice to talk with Mr. Wilson about the Girl Scout trip.

"You would like me to tell you that you may miss the last practice and still sing in the cantata, wouldn't you?" Mr. Wilson suggested. Diane nodded eagerly.

"I know all the words and music by heart, and there are still two more practices besides the last one," she said.

"I'm sorry," Mr. Wilson said, and he sounded sorry. "This is one of the few rules I have for the choir. I can't make an exception. We'll miss you and your voice if you choose to go on the trip. I would like to know as soon as possible what you plan to do. Your solo is an important part. If you aren't going to sing I'll have to find someone else as soon as possible."

Diane's face was long as she turned to go. She found Joan waiting outside. When she saw Diane's face Joan shook her head.

"The old crank," she muttered softly.

"I wish we were going today instead of next week," Joan said for what seemed the hundredth time.

"So do I," said Diane, "Then we wouldn't have to choose between singing in the cantata or going to the farm."

"I know what I'm going to do," Joan said. "I'm going to the farm. I wouldn't miss the trip for anything."

"Well I don't want to miss it either," said Diane. "But I want to sing in the cantata too. Oh, how am I going to choose which one to do?" She was still wondering when she got home.

"Mrs. Colby called," Mother said as she came in. "She says you must make up your mind about the trip. You'd better call her right away."

"I'd like to know too," Mother went on. "If you are going on the trip perhaps we should wait to buy your new dress."

"But, Mother, maybe Mr. Wilson will still change his mind if *you* speak to him. Couldn't you ask him, please?"

"Diane we have discussed that," was all Mother said.

"Isn't one of these things more important than the other?" Father broke in. "You will have to decide which one it is."

Diane looked surprised at first and then stubborn. She jumped up from the table.

"I don't think you care what's important to me," she shouted. "You're mean, you're all mean! You should help me decide." And then she ran upstairs crying.

ESTHER BAILEY

Old Clothes

Mildred pulled up the flap of the tent and peered inside. "Move over," she said, giving Ruth a shove.

Edith, Lucy, Sharon, and Ruth were huddled in the little tent in Sharon's backyard where they spent so many hours talking.

Mildred had a lot to say today. "That Debby Sterns is stuck-up. I'm not going to feel sorry for her ever again. Not as long as I live. She can go on wearing her old ragged clothes for all I care. She's hateful."

"What happened?" the others asked.

"I stopped by for her Thursday, and when the door was open I could see in. Did you ever see that place? It's a mess."

"I saw it," Sharon interrupted. "My brother and I went over and looked in the window one day when they were gone. It was terrible. There's only one bed, and there are five children. They have some old mattresses on the floor where they sleep and piles of old rags and clothes on the beds."

Mildred interrupted her, "And it smells awful too. I could hardly stay at the door."

"No wonder she never has us come over to her house to play. I feel sorry for her. I suppose she doesn't want to come here either because she's afraid we'll get too friendly and want to go there. I *do* feel sorry for her," said Edith.

"Well I don't," Mildred said. "She's hateful, and I don't care how poor they are."

"Just because she's poor and lives in a messy old place is no reason to hate her," Sharon said.

"That's what I thought, but I've changed my mind," Mildred said emphatically.

"Well, do get on and tell us what happened," Lucy begged.

"When I went home Thursday I told my mother about her place, and we talked about her clothes being so old and worn. Mother said I could take some of my things to her. So we went through my closet and found all kinds of clothes that I don't really need — my red dress, and the green plaid one, and my pink sweater, and the blue coat. We put them in a shopping bag, and I took them over to her."

"That was wonderful," Edith said. "I'll bet she was happy."

"Happy!" snorted Mildred. "Wouldn't you think she would at least have been grateful?"

"Wasn't she?" Sharon asked.

"No," Mildred was really feeling angry now that she was telling about it. "No, she took it when I gave it to her and she just stood there and didn't say anything, not even 'Thank you.'"

"Maybe she was embarrassed," said Sharon.

"I said to her, 'Let's open it so you can see what I've brought,' and I took out all the things. She didn't look pleased — just stood there and acted like she couldn't bear to look at them."

Lucy spoke thoughtfully, "Maybe Debby doesn't like to wear other people's clothes. I don't believe I'd like it if someone came to my door and handed me a bundle of old clothes."

"Of course not, stupid," Mildred told her. "You aren't poor."

"I don't think poor people like it either," Lucy said.

"Yes, they do," Sharon insisted. "We always take our old clothes and other things to a poor family down by the tracks, and they like it. They thank us and beg us to come again soon."

"Of course," Mildred agreed. "Poor people have to wear other people's clothes because they can't afford to buy new ones. They should be grateful that we think about them and want to help them. I tell you that Debby Sterns is just stuck-up — standing there like she was too good to wear my things! She made me feel foolish."

"I don't think I would like it either," Lucy said again. "I would feel like Debby. I wish she could have some new clothes, some she picked out herself."

"She wouldn't know how to take care of new clothes. She wouldn't even hang them up," Sharon said.

"I don't suppose she's ever had any new clothes. I wish she could have all new clothes just once," Lucy said.

LUCILE LINDBERG

We Like to Help

The table was covered with cans of food and bags of fruit, and the children were crowded around it.

"I brought a bag of potatoes," Luther said. "Mom didn't think anyone else would remember them."

"I brought a can of caviar," Ruth said. "See, it's marked seventy-nine cents."

"For that tiny jar, seventy-nine cents?" David asked. "That's silly, you could have got four cans of spaghetti with that money."

"I know, but Mother says there should be something special in every basket for the poor. It shouldn't be only things they need," she explained.

"Isn't turkey special enough? And I brought cranberries to go with it. Poor people probably wouldn't even know what caviar is," Sally told her.

"They will know. Everybody knows." Ruth was disgusted.

"I'm not everybody then," said Luther. "I don't know. What is it?"

"Fish eggs, silly," said Ruth.

"Who wants fish eggs?" Luther retorted. "Fish eggs! Fish eggs! How crazy can you get? A can of fish eggs to give to the poor."

He pulled himself up, put his hand out, palm up in front of him. "Help the poor! Help the poor!" he said in a plaintive voice. "Please give me a few cents to buy some fish eggs. I'm starving for fish eggs."

"Stop your nonsense," said Mrs. Jerome. "We have many wonderful foods here. There will be a fine variety."

She placed two large baskets on the table. In one they put the turkey and the potatoes and finished filling it with apples and oranges. In the other they placed all the cans. On top they put a huge bunch of bananas. Then they placed cellophane over the whole thing and tied a big red ribbon on the handle of each basket. They did look wonderful!

"Some poor family will be glad to get these. It will make a good Thanksgiving dinner for them," Mark said.

"They'll be surprised to get so many nice things," Sally said.

"It seems like quite a bit when we wrap it this way," Mrs. Jerome said. "Have you ever thought about how many groceries come into your house each week, and how many baskets it would take to hold them? This won't last very long."

"It will give them a good dinner, though, and I like to do things for people," Sally said.

"I belong to the Boy Scouts and am supposed to do a good deed every day," Luther said. "Well, I've done mine for today."

"We should help the poor," Nita said. "We have enough to eat and good clothes to wear. I like to help people — it gives me such a good feeling."

"Sometimes for my good deed I give Joe Smith a piece of candy," Larry said. "He doesn't have money for candy. I feel sorry for him and want to do something."

Miss Robinski stepped to the door.

"Mrs. Martin just phoned," she said. "Sally is to go right home as soon as school is out. Her mother wants her to stay with the baby while she goes to the dentist."

"That baby! Always that baby! I was going to stop at Ruth's to play and see her new dress. And I'm going to. They can't make me work all the time. 'Set the table!' 'Go get the butter!' 'Pick up Buddy's rattle!' 'See who is at the door!' Orders to work, that's all I hear."

"It seems to be easier to help people we don't know have a Thanksgiving dinner than to help our own families, doesn't it?" Mrs. Jerome said.

Luther agreed. "When we do this it is finished and we feel good. But when we help our own family the work is never done."

"We don't get the same feeling helping at home. I wonder why?" Mrs. Jerome said.

"It's a different kind of helping," Sally said. "It doesn't count as much as when you help the poor."

"Are you sure?" Mrs. Jerome asked. "I'm very pleased when my daughters help me. I don't know what I would do without them."

"I get a good feeling sometimes when I help Dad rake the leaves. It's fun, and we get done and go fishing. That makes me feel good. I don't like to work alone though," said one of the boys.

"Taking care of the baby doesn't make me feel good," Ruth said. "Nobody thanks me for it. Mother thinks I ought to help. I'm part of the family too, she says. It isn't special when I help her. This is special because it's charity."

LUCILE LINDBERG

It's My Sled!

"It's my turn! I want another turn!" A dozen voices were calling to Fred as he pulled the sled up the hill.

"Let me try it once more. It's my sled. I want to see how the brake works," Fred told them.

"Aw, come on, you've had two turns already." Oscar grabbed the rope from him. "I want to take it this time."

Fred was feeling angry. This was the way it had been going all morning. This was the first snow since Christmas, and now he couldn't play with his own sled. Mom had warned him this would happen when he had insisted on the fancy sled with the hand brake for Christmas.

"Well, you take it this time," Fred told Oscar. "But then I want to go down."

He wanted to share, but he had been down the hill only twice, and it was his sled.

"Take me with you. Let me go next," Irv insisted.

"I'll take you, but let me be underneath. I want to steer," Fred answered.

They stood at the top as Oscar pulled the sled up the hill.

"Hurry, won't you, we don't have all day!" Fred called.

As Oscar came up to the top of the hill Harold grabbed the rope and flung himself down on the sled. Arthur got on top of him, and Ralph ran after them and piled on top of Arthur, but he didn't get a good hold and was thrown off.

"What's the matter with you?" Fred cried out. "Don't you know anything? How many do you think that sled will hold? You want to break it, you crazy fools."

Just then he heard someone yell, "Watch it! Watch it!" And then another voice, "Look out! You're going to crash!"

Fred turned around just in time to see his sled jerk to a stop just in front of a tree stump. The two boys were thrown off the sled.

Everyone ran down the hill, with Fred in the lead. If his sled was broken Mom would blame him. She'd say he was careless with his toys, that it didn't pay to get him anything, that he didn't know how to take care of things!

"You dope," Arthur was saying to Ralph as the crowd arrived. "Why didn't you leave me alone? I had it under control until you tried to take it from me."

"Oh yeah," said Ralph. "You had it under control, did you? You were headed straight for that stump. Can't you see anything?"

Fred picked up his sled and looked it over. The brake still worked. The runners were all right, just some paint scraped off. "Gee, look at that paint," he said.

"What difference does a little paint make, Fred? It will still go. Now let's have our ride. You promised me." It was Irv pulling at his coat and insisting.

The hill seemed very long as they climbed up, and Fred was sick of this business. Just then he heard his mother call! "Fred, Fred, lunch is ready."

"That's Mom. I've got to go." He started gladly.

Irv ran up behind him. "Leave your sled here so we can play with it while you are gone. I'll look after it, honest I will. It's the best sled on the hill."

"No, I wont," Fred answered. "It's my sled. I want to take it home with me." He continued on with the others following. He wished they had asked for sleds with hand brakes if they liked them so well.

"Listen to him," said Perry. "He doesn't want to let us have it."

"Fred's a stingy. Fred's a stingy. Fred's a stingy." Susan and Beth started it, and all the boys joined in. At least they weren't following now, just yelling at him.

Fred began to walk faster. He was angry. Call him stingy — he'd show them how stingy he could be! All this time on the hill and just two rides. He wasn't going to leave his sled for them to bust.

Just then he had an idea. This afternoon he'd ask his mother to take him and his sled out into the country. Maybe she would when he told her about the morning. Then he could play with his sled all by himself. He knew what he would do too. He would go down the hill as many times as he wished.   LUCILE LINDBERG

Rena's Report Card

Rena looked at the clock. It was quarter after three and Miss Blake hadn't said anything yet. Maybe she would wait till tomorrow to pass out the report cards. The clock ticked on, and minute by minute Rena sat there hoping — hoping that they weren't ready today.

But at three twenty-five Miss Blake walked to the front of the room holding those thirty-one envelopes with a rubber band around them.

"Put your work away quickly," she said. "I want to give you your report cards before the bell rings."

"Anderson, Arnold, Bellows, Betts," Miss Blake called them off in alphabetical order.

"Calderon, D'Arcy, Eberhart," she continued.

Rena walked to the front and took her card. The room was a blur as she turned to go back. She was afraid to open it. She sat a moment before she looked at it. She hoped that some miracle had happened. Maybe Miss Blake had decided to give her good marks.

Already she could see Esther showing her A's all around. She held up one hand with the fingers spread apart to show that she had five A's.

"Hey, how do you like this? I got a D in arithmetic. Thought I'd flunk that for sure," said Joel happily from the seat across the aisle.

Rena finally slipped the card out of the envelope and opened it. She glanced quickly at it, and then tried to hold back the tears. Two failures, one in arithmetic and one in spelling. She'd known she would get them, and here they were.

Esther was beckoning to her to find out what her grades were. Rena could see her out of the corner of her eye, but she kept herself busy putting her card away and getting her books piled up to take home. She didn't want to have to tell everyone she had really failed.

When the class was dismissed she went back to her desk to get a pencil. Then she bent down to tie her shoe. If she moved slowly enough maybe all of the girls would be out of the cloak room.

No one was in sight as she put on her coat, and hat, and her mittens. Slowly she went down the steps. Even more slowly she walked down the path to the street. The girls were about a block ahead. Rena waited until they had gone around the corner. Then she turned into the side street.

She peeked around the corner, but there were the four of them standing and talking. Mavis saw her and called to her.

The others looked up, so Rena had to join them.

"You been crying?" Esther asked.

"Is it your report card?" Mavis wanted to know. "Because if it is, it isn't worth crying about. Mine is terrible. Mom will have a fit, and Dad will blow a fuse, but they'll get over it."

"But I failed two subjects," Rena sobbed. "Arithmetic and spelling."

Now it was out. They knew she had failed again.

"That teacher's lousy. She always gives low marks. Thinks she's smart, but I don't think she is," Emily burst out.

"Yeah, she's mean. Why can't she give a person a chance," Mavis added.

Rena began to catch the idea of blaming the teacher. "I'd like to tear this report card into pieces and make her swallow them. Maybe she'd choke. That's what she deserves."

"Yes, and my A's. She can have them too, so there. She doesn't know much," Esther said, trying to be a good sport. She really liked the teacher though, and was very proud of her A's.

"Ground up snakes and gooseberries are too good for her," Mavis said with glee.

"I'd like to take her to the top of Mt. Hood and then throw her off." Rena was feeling better and joined in with vigor.

"That's the trouble with teachers," Esther said. "They like to make it hard for you."

"Miss Blake thinks she's great. Miss Blake thinks she's great," Mavis chanted.

The four girls went down the street, walking in step, their arms intertwined, chanting in a chorus, "Miss Blake thinks she's great. Miss Blake thinks she's great."

Rena felt much better. She was glad the girls were on her side. But she still had to go home, and she knew how disappointed her parents would be. What would they say when they saw her report card?

LUCILE LINDBERG

Her Majesty the Queen

"If that Carol gets to play the part of the queen I won't be able to stand it! She's too stuck-up already!"

Linda's round pink face, usually jolly and full of laughter, was troubled. She gave Patty's arm a squeeze as they hurried toward school.

"Listen, Patty, you've just got to win the tryouts this afternoon!"

Patty smiled down into her friend's serious face. It was good to know that Linda was on her side. Although Linda was only going to be one of the court ladies, she hadn't seemed to mind Patty's being picked to try out for the queen. In fact, Patty decided, she'd been wonderful about it.

"I hope I don't get scared when I have to read in front of the class," Patty said. "Reading a play is different from reading out of a book. I've never had to read one before. But anyhow," she added, "Mrs. Williams says we'll all be in the play and wear fancy costumes. So, I guess it doesn't matter much who's queen. She'll just have more lines to learn, that's all."

Patty tried to sound as if it didn't matter. But deep inside she knew that she wanted to be queen more than anything else in the world. It had been an exciting moment when Mrs. Williams had picked her as one of the four best readers who might try out for the part. For the past two days Patty had imagined herself sweeping across the stage in a trailing gown, a golden crown circling her head, while all the court bowed low. But she kept reminding herself of one thing: it might be Carol who would wear the crown.

Linda must have been thinking the same thing.

"You'd make a good queen," she was saying, "because you are tall and read well. But you know Carol! She'll probably fix it up for herself somehow. She always manages to get her own way, especially with Mrs. Williams."

It was true. Whenever anything special was going on Carol always had her hand up in the air, and Mrs. Williams always noticed her.

"Yes, Carol," she would say, smiling down warmly on Carol's golden curls, "was there something you wanted to tell us?"

Then Carol would slide out of her seat, give her curls a little shake, fluff up her full, stand-out skirt and turn toward the class. Sometimes what she had to say didn't seem very important, but Mrs. Williams always listened.

"That Carol gives me a pain!" Patty remarked. "But some of the girls seem to like her."

"Yes, because the teacher likes her," Linda answered. "They think that by being friendly with Carol, Mrs. Williams will be nice to them too. I hate teachers who have pets. Besides," she added thoughtfully, "Carol can be sort of mean when you don't get along with her."

Patty nodded. She remembered a couple of times when she'd opposed Carol. Carol had been angry for a long time and had even gotten some of the other girls to be mad at Patty too.

"Did you know that Carol got permission yesterday to hang her coat in Mrs. Williams' closet?" Patty asked.

"Yes, I was there when Carol came in," answered Linda. "Mrs. Williams said, 'Why Carol! What a lovely new coat! Don't you look pretty!' and then Carol twirled around to show it off. I had on a new dress, but Mrs. Williams didn't even notice me. I can't see what's so great about Carol, even if she does come to school all dressed up."

"Maybe it's because her mother is at school so much," Patty said. "She's always helping out on some committee. I guess she's friendly with all the teachers."

Linda sighed. Her own mother worked in a downtown office and didn't have much time for school activities.

"It isn't fair," she said. "Carol has the prettiest clothes, her mother's always doing special things for her, and on top of that she's the teacher's favorite. It makes me mad. I hope nobody votes for her."

They were inside the school now. There was the familiar smell of chalk, and freshly waxed floors, and varnished desks, while about the room there was an air of excitement as if this were going to be a special kind of day.

A sudden flurry near the door caught Patty's eye. Carol burst in, followed by two other girls. In her hand was a grey paper bag. She hurried to the desk where Mrs. Williams was arranging some books.

"My mother sent this," she said, "to see if you could use it for part of the page boy's costume. There's a jacket to match."

Thrusting her hand into the bag she brought out a dark red velvet hat with a billowing ostrich plume curling from the brim. A chorus of excited "Oh's" went up.

Mrs. Williams held the hat admiringly.

"My isn't it handsome! Thank you, Carol. Indeed we can use it. Tell your mother how much I appreciate her sending it."

Carol was digging something else out of the bag. "Oh, and here's the play," she said, handing Mrs. Williams a roll of type-written papers. Mrs. Williams glanced at it briefly and tucked it into her desk drawer.

Patty's chest tightened in alarm. "The play. Was that what she had said? What was Carol doing with the play? Could she have been practicing for the tryouts? But Mrs. Williams wouldn't let her. It wouldn't be fair." Patty thought that maybe she had heard wrong, so she went over to the closet where Carol was hanging up her coat.

"Was that a copy of the play you just gave Mrs. Williams?" she asked.

Carol was intent on tucking her scarf into the coat pocket.

"Yes," she answered, without glancing up. "Any objections?"

Patty gasped. "You mean Mrs. Williams let you take it home and practice?"

"For your information," Carol said, "my mother's going to help with the costumes and scenery. Mrs. Williams sent the play home so she could read it and see what was needed."

"I'll bet you read it too," exclaimed Patty indignantly.

"I just read over the queen's part while my mother read the other parts. Is that all right with you?"

"I don't think it's fair," Patty burst out. "It's almost like cheating, if you ask me."

"Well, nobody *is* asking you," Carol said. She walked away quickly to get the watering pot. It was her week to tend the plants.

Patty's cheeks burned. She stared helplessly at Carol's retreating back, while a wave of anger shook her. She had a sudden impulse to snatch the watering can from Carol's hand and empty it over her head. She wanted to soak the pretty curls and the starched blue dress. She blinked back her tears. There was nothing she could do. Nothing! Mrs. Williams was on Carol's side — Mrs. Williams, smiling and pretending to be fair, always so right about everything. "I hate her!" thought Patty. "I hate them both."

She tried to pay attention during arithmetic time, but she could hardly hear Mrs. Williams' words. She kept seeing Carol studying her lines with her mother's help. Twice in the reading group Patty lost her place as she thought of Carol — Carol smiling as Mrs. Williams handed her the play to take home. The time dragged endlessly.

Finally the important work was done. Mrs. Williams stood up to make the long awaited announcement.

"Boys and girls," she said, "it's time for our tryouts. I've chosen certain children who have the right appearance for the main characters. We'll let them read their parts, and then we'll vote on the best ones. Let's start with the king."

Three boys came up and took turns reading the king's part while Mrs. Williams read the lines in between. Billy Andrews acted so silly Mrs. Williams had to scold him twice. Bob Green read his part very carefully and slowly, but the words sounded stiff and wooden. Mrs. Williams shook her head.

"Bob, you'll have to put a lot more expression into it," was all she said.

When David Gilbert started to read everyone exchanged favorable glances. He was one of the best liked boys in the grade. His voice came out firm and strong, and he seemed to know just the right places to pause.

"That's fine, David," Mrs. Williams said enthusiastically. "Now let's have the vote."

As everyone expected, David won by a large margin.

"Now for the queen's part," said Mrs. Williams.

Patty's heart skipped a beat as she stepped forward along with the other girls. Each would read only a few lines, Mrs. Williams had explained, because it would take too long to read more.

Judy read with lots of expression, but her voice sounded rather tiny.

"I don't know," Mrs. Williams said doubtfully. "You'd have to speak up much louder than that to be heard." She shook her head.

Sandy raced through the lines as if she could hardly wait to finish. Patty watched Mrs. Williams' face and could see that she wasn't pleased.

"Slow down, Sandy," she kept saying. But Sandy couldn't seem to slow down.

"Maybe I do have a chance," Patty thought, with a surge of excitement. Then suddenly it was her turn. Patty heard herself start to read. Her words came out clearly and slowly, just as she'd planned. She tried hard to put expression into the lines as if she were talking to somebody. But she had to read one line over again because she hadn't quite understood the meaning the first time and it hadn't sounded right.

"Very good, Patty," she heard Mrs. Williams say as she sat down. Now it was Carol's turn.

Carol took the paper, glanced around the room, and started to read. Every word came out clearly, and she put in little gestures as she went along. When she was supposed to say, "Ho hum!" and yawn, she fluttered her eyelids sleepily and patted her mouth with her hand. When she finished she looked up at the class, smiled, and made a little curtsy. Mrs. Williams' face shone.

"Excellent, Carol!" she exclaimed.

Patty held her breath while the vote was taken. Not many hands went up for the first two girls. "I've still got a chance," she thought. Then the hands went up for Patty. There were quite a few. Eleven, Mrs. Williams counted. Patty crossed her fingers as the vote was taken for Carol. It seemed as though a forest of hands went up. Everyone was counted twice to make sure. Fifteen! Patty tried to keep the disappointment from showing in her face. She had lost by only four votes!

"Patty, I'm going to ask you to be understudy for the queen," Mrs. Williams was saying. "You'll play the part of a court lady, but in case Carol gets sick you'll be our substitute. You'll have to know the queen's part. That's how it is done in the real theatre," she added. "The understudy is a very important person."

Patty nodded. She tried to look satisfied. But the ache inside was hard to put down. Carol was smiling happily. Patty could almost see the crown circling her curls, the crown she had come so close to wearing. If only *she* had been able to study the part at home. If only her mother were helping with the costumes — —

At last school was over. Patty hurried out as fast as she could so that she wouldn't have to walk with anyone. She couldn't bear to talk about the play, to pretend that it was all right being understudy. She didn't even want to think about the play anymore, or about Carol or Mrs. Williams. Besides, she had planned to return a book that was overdue at the library. She was glad to have an excuse for hurrying on ahead.

It was quiet and peaceful in the library. Patty paid her fine at the desk and stepped over to the juvenile section to find a book. Squatting on her heels she began to scan the titles on the row of books behind one of the tables. Behind her was a scuffle of feet as several newcomers wandered in. Patty didn't bother to glance up. There was a flurry of whispers and giggles.

"Psst!" somebody whispered loudly. "Here's a book that gives me an idea for Carol: *Queenie, the Wonder Dog.* What do you say, let's start calling her 'Queenie.'" The others giggled.

"Queenie the Meanie!" another said. More giggles.

"I voted for her, though." It sounded like Ginny Mills. "She'll be good in the part, even if she isn't so good in some other ways."

"I voted for her too. She's the one Mrs. Williams wanted. But she sure is stuck on herself."

There was a moment's silence. Patty didn't know what to do. The girls couldn't see her. And now it was too late to stand up and let them know she'd heard.

"I voted for Patty. I like her lots better," said a voice.

"Me too. But we weren't supposed to vote for the one we liked best. Patty's not as queenlike as 'Queenie.' A queen's supposed to be someone who's good at acting important."

"I read in a book once about a queen who thought she was so important everyone got to hate her. The people finally had a revolution and ordered her head chopped off."

"Boy! That Queenie must have been a real meanie!" Then they all giggled again.

"Girls!" The librarian had hurried over. "You're being too noisy," she said quietly. "Have you found your books yet?"

The girls were suddenly quiet. They drifted over to the desk and in a few minutes they were gone.

Patty rose from her cramped position. As she checked out her book and headed out into the afternoon wind her thoughts were on the conversation she'd overheard. She felt a little guilty at having listened, but she was glad too. At least some of the girls who voted for Carol didn't really like her better. It was Mrs. Williams who liked Carol. Probably she had planned to give Carol the part right from the beginning.

"She's the worst teacher I ever had!" Patty thought fiercely. "I hate her! I wish I dared say so right to her face."

Suddenly she was aware of a voice in the distance calling her name. She turned to see Linda hurrying to catch up with her.

"Hi!" puffed Linda. "I've been chasing you for a whole block. Didn't you hear me calling?"

"No," said Patty. "I guess I was thinking of something else."

"About the play, I'll bet," said Linda. "I'm so mad to think Carol got the part. Curtseying, and smiling, and blinking her eyes at the teacher. Ugh!" Linda made a face. "A lot of the kids are saying it wasn't a fair tryout."

"I'll say it wasn't fair," broke in Patty. "There was nothing fair about it! Carol even had a chance to practice at home."

"I know. That's what the kids are saying. I hope she can't be

in the play. Then you'd get the part. I'm glad you're the understudy, anyway."

"Understudy, humph!" snorted Patty. "Who wants that?"

Linda looked surprised. "Well, jeepers, it's better than I got.
I never even had a chance to try out, neither did most of the other
girls. I guess just about everybody would have liked to be the
queen."

Patty stared thoughtfully at Linda.

"Yes, but I *almost* was. I might have been too, if Mrs. Williams
had been fair. That makes it worse."

"I think it's worse not to have a chance in the first place." Linda
glanced down at her stubby brown oxfords. "She wouldn't even
let me read the part because she said I didn't have the right appearance. Maybe," she said slowly, "she thought I was too fat."

"Why, you're not fat!" Patty declared hotly. "You'd look good
in a long costume. But you should worry, Linda. Maybe you don't
look the way Mrs. Williams thinks a queen should, but you look
nice. And you act nice. I'd rather have you around any day than
Carol, even if she is queen."

Linda's face brightened. "That's funny," she said thoughtfully,
"That's what some of the kids were saying about you!"

"They were?" Patty peered into Linda's friendly face and
somehow began to feel better. She was still angry, but along with
the angry feeling a new idea was forming in her mind.

"You know," she said, "Carol really will make a good queen.
Maybe the kids would have voted for her anyway, because you
know nobody can beat Carol for acting queenlike."

"Stuck-up, you mean," sniffed Linda. They walked along
silently a little way.

"It ought to be a pretty play with all those bright costumes,"
Linda remarked. "Mrs. Williams says we can each pick the color
we want. And you know what else? We're supposed to wear
sparkling jewelry too."

"Oh, my mother has some beautiful rhinestone jewelry, a
whole box full!" cried Patty. "I know she'll let us borrow some.
It would be perfect for court costumes. Won't it be beautiful, with
all those bright costumes and sparkling jewelry?"

"I'll bet it will be the prettiest play put on in assembly this year," Linda said.

"I just know it will," agreed Patty.

MARGARET RITCHIE

War Games

Five boys were playing war on the neighborhood playground one Saturday afternoon. The sixth sat on a bench and watched. Dan watched the battle and wished his father wouldn't be so strict about his not playing in the war games. John looked very real as he staggered, clutched his chest and fell.

"Hey, Dan, come on and join us," Gregory shouted at him.

"Aw, leave him alone," Rob said as Dan hesitated. "He'll spoil the game. Besides, you know he hasn't any gun."

Suddenly Dan jumped up from the bench.

"I don't need a gun." He picked up a piece of pipe from the ground and aimed at Rob. "Bang!"

"Come on," Brian shouted. "We've got an hour to find that transmitter." He ducked behind an imaginary rock and took aim.

Dan joined the game and fought with the rest, although he didn't feel right about it. The air was filled with shouts, groans, loud bangs, and sounds of machine guns. The sun grew hot, and finally, one by one, the boys stayed where they fell on the warm concrete.

"Whew," Brian wiped the sweat from his forehead. "I wonder what it's like to fight in a real battle?"

"The way you read in books and see in movies, I guess. Noise and flames and smoke all over the place," John said as he started over to the water fountain.

"And people getting wounded and killed all over the place too," said one of the boys.

"Yes, but if a soldier's smart and remembers everything he was taught in training he can keep from getting killed."

Rob snorted. "Boy are you dumb, Brian! A person gets killed if a bomb explodes on top of him whether he's smart or not."

"My dad was in two wars and he didn't even get wounded," Gregory said proudly. "He says it's all luck whether you get killed or not. He just missed getting hit dozens of times. He was brave, though. He got a medal."

Dan was scratching the concrete with his piece of iron pipe. "I bet he killed a lot of people," he said.

"So — — " Gregory started, but he was interrupted by John, who said, "My father was in the war before I was born. He hopes I'll never have to fight in one."

"You think there'll ever be another war?" Brian asked, turning lazily over on his stomach.

"Sure, there are always wars. My dad says people can't help having them," Rob answered cheerfully.

"If there is another, a really big one, nobody would win," John said, and added, "Everybody would be wiped out. That's what my dad says."

"Well, there wouldn't have to be a single war if it weren't for people being so stupid and thinking that's the only way to do things," Dan broke in.

But Rob was having none of that, "I suppose you'd let another country run all over you, and — — "

"That's why there are wars, because people think that it is the only way to settle — — "

"Aw, stop preaching Dan," Rob interrupted. "That's the trouble with you. We can't ever let you play with us without your preaching to us about something your father says."

"Oh, is that so?" Dan's face was red and angry.

"Yes, that is so," Rob said, mimicking him, and the other boys all laughed. "And what's more," he went on, "your father must be pretty stupid not to let you play with old toy guns in our games. Boy! Wait until he finds out that you've been playing with us today!" Rob whistled and rolled his eyes upward, then ducked as an object sailed past his ear, and Dan's piece of iron pipe clattered on the concrete behind him. The boys all looked at Dan.

"Temper, temper," Rob taunted. "Mustn't get angry now. You might start a fight."

"Aw, stop that, you two," Gregory said. Brian stood up.

"It's time I started home. What about the rest of you?" He looked at Dan and Rob, who had stood up and were facing each other.

Rob's grinning face looked large and blurred to Dan. Then suddenly he sprang at Rob, his fists hitting out in all directions. Sure, his father had said there was no sense to fighting, but Rob was asking for it. He'd been asking for a fight all morning, and Dan had to fight him whether it made sense or not.

"Oh, break it up, you two." Gregory turned to the others. "Come on, let's go home." The four boys walked away, across the playground, leaving Rob and Dan behind.

ESTHER BAILEY

IV
Children with handicaps

How Long a Jump?

"Please pass the peas, Bob."

"What did you say?" said Bob.

"Bob, whatever is the matter with you?" asked his mother.

Bob was sitting at the dinner table, his elbows next to his plate and his hands on his head.

"If you don't feel well maybe you'd better go up to bed," his father said.

"Oh I'm okay," he answered. "I just can't eat. I'm thinking about that achievement test I can't pass."

"I thought they only gave those at the end of the school year," remarked his father. "How do you happen to be having them now?"

"Oh these aren't at school," Bob said. "I mean the one for the Cub Scouts. I have to pass them to become a Webelos, and I can't get one of them."

"What seems to be the trouble?" asked his mother.

"It's that old broad jump," Bob said. "I can do everything but that one. I had three tries today, and I couldn't jump the seven feet in any of them."

"Are all the other boys Webelos already?" asked father.

"Oh no, most of the other fellows have two or three more tests to do."

"Well I'm sure you'll get it soon if you keep on practicing," said his father. "Meanwhile, will you pass me the peas?"

Every afternoon that week Bob practiced some broad jumps in his back yard. A few times he almost did the seven foot jump, and once he even went beyond it. He began to look forward eagerly to the next Cub Scout meeting.

Larry, Alfred, and Joseph were already there when Bob arrived at Mrs. Corin's for the den meeting. They talked eagerly among themselves about what tests they still had to pass. A car rolled up the driveway, and Mrs. Kent opened the door for Fred and started to lead him up to the house by taking his arm.

"I'm okay. Please let me walk by myself," the boys heard Fred say. When Joseph opened the door he saw Mrs. Kent standing at the bottom of the steps while Fred felt his way into the house.

Fred had joined the den last fall. He was the same age as the rest of them, but he wasn't in the same class at school because he was blind and was going to a special school where he was learning to read Braille.

"Hey, let's go outside," said Joseph. "There's a rope hanging from a tree for you fellows to practice on, and lots of room for us all to try the broad jump."

"That's a good idea," said Bob. "I'll show you how far I can jump now."

The boys were all charging through the door when Alfred noticed Fred. He was slowly getting out of the chair and coming over where he heard their voices. "Are we going outside?" he asked.

"Yeah, we're going to practice before Philip comes. Don't you want to come with us?"

"Sure," said Fred. "I need to practice too."

The boys divided into two groups, one to practice rope climbing and the other doing the broad jump.

"Hey, watch me," yelled Bob as he ran to get a good start for his broad jump.

"Good," said the other boys as Bob landed on his feet. "The only trouble is it isn't quite seven feet."

"Is the way clear now?" Fred called, walking over to the place where they jumped.

"Sure is," answered Bob. "I'll give a whistle when you get to the starting line."

Fred took a running start and then he jumped. It didn't seem to bother him that he couldn't see as long as he knew the way was clear. "How much did I do?" he asked.

"You went a little past the four foot mark," shouted Joseph. "That's wonderful. You only have to do three and a half feet don't you?"

"That's what Philip and Mrs. Corin said," Fred answered. Then he went on, "Anyone willing to see if my story is okay?" He took two cloth puppets out of his pocket. Telling a story was part of the achievement test too, and this was easy for Fred. "Is there a table out here anywhere?" he asked.

"Yeah, here's one in front of the tree," said Larry.

"If I sit on the ground I can give you a sort of puppet show while I tell my story," said Fred, smiling proudly. "My mother taught me how to do it." He felt the table with his hands and then sat down. He fixed the puppets on his hands. "Are they straight?" he asked.

"Gee, they're wonderful." The boys were pleased with the idea of seeing the puppets, and they were ready to rest awhile anyway.

So Fred told his story about a captain and a pirate, and he moved the puppets around as he told it. Larry and Bob were really sorry to have the story end. They clapped hard and told Fred how good it was.

"Thought you guys were going to practice jumping till I got here. What are you all sitting on the ground for?" It was Philip, a senior scout who came over to help with their meetings. It was he who decided if they had passed their tests or not.

"We were watching Fred practice his story," Bob explained. "Wait till you get to that test. It's good!"

"I bet it is," said Philip. "Let's begin our meeting so that we have time for everything."

They went inside where they recited the pledge of allegiance, the Cub Scout promise, and the law of the pack. Then they talked about what they were going to do for parents' night when some of the boys were hoping to get their Lion badges and become Webelos. Before this part of the meeting was over Fred gave his puppet show again for the whole den.

"Very good, Fred," said Philip. "Now let's see," he was checking in his book, "You have just to pass the knot test and the broad jump."

"Can I do the knot test now?" asked Fred, pulling a piece of rope from his pocket. Without even waiting to hear Philip's answer Fred began to pull and twist the rope. The boys could see that the knot was perfect.

"Excellent," said Philip. "Now do the others."

When Fred was finished with the knots the boys huddled around Philip to see what they still had to do for their badges. "Most of you have outdoor tests," said Philip. "Let's go out and I will test some of you."

Joseph and Peter passed the rope test the first time they tried, but Alfred couldn't seem to manage it. Then Larry tried the broad jump and he made seven and a half feet, so he passed.

"Boy, you sure must have practiced a lot," said Bob. "I hope I pass."

He got a running start and then made the jump. "Five and a half feet," said Philip. "I guess you have to practice another week. You were doing better than that last meeting. Don't be so worried and you'll jump better."

"Can I try now," said Fred eagerly.

"Okay. Out of the way, boys," said Philip.

Fred came running and covered four feet again.

"Good!" said Philip. "You've earned your Lion's badge now. Be sure to be there on parents' night to get it!"

"Please," pleaded Bob. "I know I can pass the test. I just needed a little warming up."

"Okay, but just once more," warned Philip.

This time Bob started way down at the other end of the driveway. All the boys watched as he made his jump.

"Well, it's six feet this time," Philip reported. "I can't pass you yet, but you're doing better. Maybe you'll have better luck next time."

Philip left then, and the boys were standing around. "Don't worry," said Alfred, "some of us still have a lot of tests to pass. In fact, Fred is the only one who is sure he'll get his badge."

"Yeah, you're a lucky guy!" said Joseph. "But you had easier tests to pass. Anyone could pass if he only had four feet to jump."

Fred's mother had come, and he was walking toward the car. Bob really thought he was out of earshot when he added, "I don't think it's fair. Just because he is blind he gets away with anything. It's just like *giving* him a badge."

Then they heard Mrs. Kent say, "Why Fred, what's the matter? You look sad. Didn't the puppet show go well?" But they couldn't hear what Fred answered. They all looked at each other and didn't say anything for a minute.   JANET GIVENS

Sally's Homework

Isabel ran into the house crying. "Mother, Mother, where are you?"

"Here I am, Isabel. What is the matter?" answered her mother.

"Oh, Mother, we just did something awful, but we didn't mean to." Isabel started to cry again, and so did Joyce, who had come in with her.

"Now, now," said Mrs. Blanchard. "It can't be anything so terrible. Tell me about it."

Both girls started to talk at once.

"You see we didn't know — — "

"Let me tell it — — "

"How could we have known — — "

Mrs. Blanchard looked puzzled. "Isabel, you start. Then Joyce, you tell me the rest. I can't figure anything out when you both talk at once and are half crying at the same time. Suppose you sit a minute and think what you are going to say."

The girls sat still for a few minutes, and they did feel more calm. Then Isabel started to tell the story.

"Mother, you know that new girl that moved in down the street? We went down to play with her. She looks about our age. So we went up and started to talk to her."

"But she didn't pay any attention," said Joyce. "She didn't even turn around and look at us. She acted as if she didn't know we were there."

"So," Isabel went on, "we thought she was daydreaming. We jumped on the stair beside her and covered her eyes with our hands."

"Yes, and then Isabel said, 'New friends! Guess our names!'" added Joyce. "But she just jumped up as though she were scared and ran in the house."

"Then her mother came out. She said we were mean and scolded us for teasing her. She told us to go right home and leave her alone."

"But we weren't teasing. Honest we weren't," Joyce said. "We feel terrible. We just wanted to be friends."

Mother looked troubled. She said, "I don't really know what the story is, girls. Why don't you let me go down and find out. You play with the baby for me, so I can go. I'll be right back. I'm sure there must be more than we know about."

The girls felt better now that they had talked about it. They took the baby out of the play pen and walked him around the house for a while. Then they got some toys for him to play with. Before they knew it, Mother was back.

"It was a misunderstanding, girls," Mother said. "I talked to the lady. Her name is Mrs. Downer. The girl is deaf, and she did not hear you coming up the walk. That's why she paid no attention. And she was startled when you covered her eyes, because she could not hear what you said. Mrs. Downer only knew the girl had come in crying. She looked out just as you covered her eyes. She is sorry she scolded you, but where they lived before the children teased Sally because she wasn't like the rest of them."

"She's deaf? She can't hear anything at all? How awful!" Isabel said.

"That's right, she has never heard a sound or a word in her life. Most of the time she is away from home at a school where she is going to learn to talk, but she can't say anything yet. She isn't twelve like you — she's only ten. She is a big girl for her age."

"Oh, Mother," said Isabel. "No wonder Mrs. Downer thought we were mean. But we would play with her, really we would. We wouldn't mind her being deaf. Isn't there something we can do to let her know?"

"I talked with Mrs. Downer about that too," answered Mother. "She said that she would like to have you come down. Sally is going to do her homework, and she thought maybe you would like to watch. Then she has some games you could play together. She says Sally needs children to play with."

"Homework? How can she do that when she can't hear and doesn't know how to talk?" It was Joyce asking now.

"Why don't you run along and see?"

The girls were a little hesitant as they went up the walk, but Mrs. Downer was standing in the door smiling. Sally was smiling too. "I'm sorry, girls," Mrs. Downer said, "but I misunderstood what you were doing. Would you like to see Sally do her lessons? That will give her a chance to get acquainted with you. She is very shy."

"Oh, yes," said the girls.

They sat down at the table and watched. Mrs. Downer had the table full of little objects, and Sally was sitting on the other side. Mrs. Downer leaned over and put her hand on Sally, then Sally stopped looking at the girls and looked at her mother.

"Give me the doll," said Mrs. Downer. Sally did!

"Oh, she heard you, she heard you," cried Joyce.

Mrs. Downer shook her head. "No, she can't hear, but she is learning to read my lips. It takes a very long time. She knows quite a few words now, but we didn't learn about this school until a year ago. If only we had known about it when she was smaller."

The lesson went on for about fifteen minutes. Sally knew a lot of the words, but sometimes she made mistakes. She gave her mother a picture of a house when she asked for a horse. She took a picture of a store when her mother asked for a door. But most of the time she got them right.

Mrs. Downer kept smiling. "Good, Sally, good," she would say and clap her hands. "Now we will play some games." She turned to the girls. "This game is like Lotto, but we only have words on the card that Sally has learned. Do you want to play?"

They had a lot of fun playing. They smiled at Sally, and she smiled at them. Sometimes they forgot and said things to her, but then they'd just smile again. Then Mrs. Downer came in with cocoa. After they drank it she played some records for them. Sally sat with her hand on the edge of the machine.

"She can feel the music," Mrs. Downer explained, "but she can't hear it. After a while she will learn to keep time to the rhythm, and some day she will be able to dance. It all takes a lot of time."

Then it was time to go home. "Thank you, Mrs. Downer," said Isabel and Joyce.

"Thank you, girls, for coming over. I hope you will come and play with Sally again."

Then they really had a surprise! Mrs. Downer looked at Sally carefully, and very slowly she said, "Say good-by."

Sally hesitated a minute, and then although it was hard to understand it, she did say it! "Good-by, good-by."

"Good-by, Sally," chorused Joyce and Isabel as they walked away together.

DOROTHY SPOERL

His Face Looks Funny

Late afternoon at the neighborhood pool was always the best. At least Kathy thought so. There weren't too many people there then. When the pool wasn't crowded Mommie would play tag in the baby pool. Sometimes boys and girls who were in the pool would play too. When Mommie was "it" she pretended to be fierce. The boys and girls would yell to each other as they scrambled out of her way.

"Oh, here comes the giant," Janet squealed. She stumbled and flopped on her face in the water. She was trying to get away from Mommie, who was crawling on her stomach and making gurgling noises all the way across the pool. Kathy tried to follow Janet. In her excitement she fell over backwards. Kathy didn't see the little boy in a rubber tube bobbing in the water near her.

"Kathy, watch what you are doing!"

It was Mother's serious voice, and it surprised Kathy because they had been having such fun being silly. She tried to stand up. Instead she fell into the little boy who had floated close to her.

The little boy started to cry. Kathy looked at him. His face looked funny. Then she looked at him hard. She didn't like the looks of him. She felt uncomfortable. She hadn't meant to make him cry, but she didn't know what to say.

The boy's father leaned over the edge of the pool and pulled the boy toward him. "It's all right," he said to Kathy. "Don't mind. He was just surprised."

Mother had decided by then that their game was too rough for the baby pool. She said they had better go to swim in the big pool. On her way out, Kathy looked at the boy again. He had almost stopped crying. He was almost as big as she was, but he wasn't talking at all. He was making grunty kinds of sounds. Kathy noticed that his daddy was very nice to him.

As they walked home from the pool together, Kathy said to her mother, "Why did that boy look different? I didn't like his face."

"Do you mean the little boy you bumped into?" Mother said. "He looked different because he was born without the ways to think and talk that people usually have. Instead of being born without an arm, by accident, he was born without ways to think the way we can."

"I hope my baby isn't born like that. I'd feel very sad if I had a baby like that. Why does his face look so funny?"

"It doesn't look funny to me. I think it bothered you because he didn't look as though he were paying attention to anything." Then her mother went on, "People do feel sad to have a child that can never be the way other people are. But they learn to know what things are fun for him to do, what he likes, what makes him sad, and they find they love him even though it is hard to know him. You are right — it is sad because there are so many things he can't ever understand."

"Will he ever talk, Mommie?"

"Maybe — a few words anyway. If he goes to a school where people pay special attention to him, he'll learn quite a few things."

Several days later Kathy and her friend were walking to the schoolyard to swing. Kathy noticed a boy coming down the side street toward them. He ran in a jerky sort of way, like a little boy would, even though he looked almost as tall as Kathy. She realized it was the boy that she and her mother had seen at the pool.

Cindy giggled the silly giggle she had sometimes and said, "Oh, here comes that boy. John says he's crazy."

Kathy felt funny, but not like giggling. She felt too serious inside to make fun the way Cindy was. She tried not to listen to Cindy's chattering. She watched the boy running toward the street. "That can't be right," she thought. "Mommie said he doesn't understand. He wouldn't know about the street."

She stopped, but Cindy grabbed her hand and yelled, "Let's run."

"You go ahead," Kathy said. And Cindy ran on.

The little boy looked up and stopped walking. Kathy went slowly toward him. He grinned as he had at the pool. Kathy said, "Hi." He just stood there. Kathy didn't know what else to say. She asked, "Where do you live?"

The little boy grinned and made a sound. Then he bumped into her and smacked his hands on either side of her face. Kathy laughed. She felt just like she did when the baby next door cooed at her. She reached out and took his hand. They walked down the sidewalk together.

Kathy didn't know where the little boy lived, but she knew it wasn't right for him to be out alone. It was a short way to her house, and Mommie would know what to do.

From behind, Kathy heard a woman's voice calling. She looked around and saw a lady running down the side street. When the woman saw Kathy holding the little boy's hand she stopped running and walked toward them.

"Thank you," she said. "He got out of the yard. I didn't see him go." Kathy thought the lady sounded almost as if she were going to cry.

"That's all right," Kathy said. "I thought he wasn't supposed to be out by himself."

The lady smiled at her. "Come to see us sometime. We live in that yellow house over there. Brian would enjoy having you come to play. He gets lonely all by himself."

Kathy nodded her head and smiled back. Then she turned and walked faster and faster until she was running. All the way home she thought about the way Brian had smiled at her, and she could hardly wait to tell how glad his mother had been that she had helped.

EILEEN DAY

It's Hard to Remember

Miss Rathburn finished talking to the principal and turned to the class.

"It's good news," she said. "Al Holt will be back with us on Monday."

The class let out a cheer as they clapped and pounded on their desks. It was good news.

Miss Rathburn held up both hands signaling them to stop. "It is wonderful. I feel like shouting myself. It has been so long since he was hurt. We shall look forward to his coming back, but we will need to do some planning. He'll need help from all of us."

Al Holt had been in an automobile accident in October. His legs had been badly crushed and for weeks he had been in the hospital in the city. They had been told he would never be able to walk again. The children had written to him regularly, and they had sent him cards and books and pictures. In February he had come home in an ambulance.

After that some of his special friends had been dropping in to see him regularly. And now he was coming back to school!

"He has to stay in his wheel chair all the time. How will he get up the stairs with it every day? I suppose his father will have to help him," one of the children said.

"That is what Miss Smith and I were just discussing," Miss Rathburn told him. "We are going to trade rooms with Miss Spellman's class. We'll do it this afternoon."

"You mean we are going to have to move all our stuff down stairs?" Fred asked.

"That's just what I mean. Then Al can go with us when we go out on the playground."

"We can take turns pushing him, and staying with him so he won't get lonesome," Hazel said.

"He'll want to help himself with many things," Miss Rathburn reminded them. "We don't want to make him feel helpless. I think he would like our company. He can't play ball, but some of us can stand with him and talk about what is happening. Maybe he can throw the ball sometimes. We don't know yet what he can do."

"Let's form committees," suggested Ruth.

Hazel was thinking. "I don't think we should have committees," she decided. "That makes it seem as if he is just another job — like watering the plants."

"Maybe we can all be thoughtful and keep our eyes on him," Pete said.

"We can try that and see how it works," Miss Rathburn said.

When Al came on Monday morning everyone was excited. His father wheeled him in and put his chair in the place they had fixed for it.

When they sang Fred handed him a book. Pete helped him put a board across his lap when it was time for spelling, so he could write his words too. At recess time there were many hands to open doors as he wheeled himself out. There were always boys and girls to talk to him. This was an exciting adventure for all of them.

Wednesday was Ralph's birthday. His mother was bringing ice cream and cake for everyone. The class was on the playground when her car drove to the end of the walk. Ralph was watching and ran to help her. Pete went too, and as the others saw what was happening they all ran to the car.

"What an escort I have," Ralph's mother laughed as she entered the classroom.

Miss Rathburn had cleared a table and they all stood around as Ralph's mother put on a paper table cloth and unwrapped the cake. What a beautiful cake it was!

"We'd better serve before the ice cream melts," she said to Miss Rathburn.

"Get in your seats quickly children," Miss Rathburn said. "It will be easier to serve you."

Suddenly Larry said, "Where's Al?"

The space they had made for his wheel chair was empty! The room became very quiet.

All eyes turned to the window. There he was, all alone, wheeling himself up to the building. Fred ran down the hall to help him through the door.

But the rest of the children sat in silence, stunned as they realized what they had done.

It was Ruth who broke the silence. "We had such good intentions," she said, "but the first time something special happened we forgot all about Al."

LUCILE LINDBERG

The Lost Ball

Tommy and the other boys in the neighborhood all called it the "haunted house."

It wasn't really haunted, of course, but the boys liked to pretend it was. The overgrown shrubbery and half-closed blinds gave the place a neglected look, and when Mrs. Warren, who lived there with her two cats, came out muttering and scolding it was easy to imagine that she was a real witch.

For there was no doubt about it — Mrs. Warren was a queer old lady. Tommy had heard some of the neighbors say that she was insane. He asked his father what that meant, and Dad had explained it meant she was "sick in the head."

She was thin and bony, with piercing blue eyes that peered suspiciously from beneath the limp ruffle of the little cap she always wore. Often the children glimpsed her peeking cautiously out from behind the shrubbery, or from behind her blinds, ready to shout at them to leave her alone if they loitered in front of her house.

Nobody ever seemed to visit her. The only times she came out of the house were to chase the children away, or to putter in her garden, or to air her cats. There was a sleek yellow one, and a fat grey Persian, both with fancy little collars.

Mrs. Warren would hitch their leashes to the clothesline so that the cats could play in the grass without running away. All the time she would be talking, half out loud, shaking her head angrily as if she were scolding someone. With her yardstick she would poke carefully in the bushes, muttering about "spies" and "time bombs." Then, satisfied that everything was safe, she would stroke her cats and disappear into the house.

"I think she likes cats better than children," Tommy complained to his mother one day after Mrs. Warren had chased the children off the front sidewalk.

"That's because she trusts her cats," his mother said. "She knows they love her and she doesn't have to be afraid of them."

To Tommy it didn't make much sense. It didn't make sense, either, when his father issued firm orders to stay away from Mrs. Warren's yard.

"But Dad," protested Tommy, "We kids don't really do anything to her."

"Mrs. Warren is suspicious, Tommy. She can't see what people really do. She sees what she expects them to do. She expects to be hurt, so the least little thing makes her jump. You might call it 'jumping to conclusions.'"

"What does that mean?"

"It means making up your mind without looking at all the facts."

"That's Mrs. Warren, all right," agreed Tommy. "I should think she was old enough to know better."

"She's been doing it so long," his father replied, "there's nothing much can change her. But at least we can try not to make her feel worse. Just stay away. Promise?"

Tommy had agreed. He and the other boys carefully avoided Mrs. Warren's yard, and for several weeks everything was quiet around the haunted house.

Then, unexpectedly, trouble broke out again.

It happened one afternoon. Tommy, Bob Frazier, and Joe Larkin had been chasing each other all the way home with Tommy's new "crazy ball." It was a different kind of ball with a weight inside that made it shoot off in unexpected directions. When Tommy had first seen it downtown three weeks ago he had decided right away that it was worth saving every penny of his allowance for. He had hardly been able to wait to show it off, and just as he'd expected, it caused a near riot.

Bob was really keen about the ball, and when he suggested a game of dodge ball on the way home, Tommy was glad for a chance to show off what the ball could do.

They had been chasing it in and out of yards so fast they didn't realize they had almost reached Mrs. Warren's house. As Bob suddenly gave the ball a wild fling it veered sharply, bounced along a driveway, and rolled under some bushes. Bob started after it, then stopped suddenly.

"Oh, oh!" he yelled. "It's in Mrs. Warren's yard."

"Well, hurry up! Get it!" Tommy yelled back.

Bob glanced nervously at the house. At the window there was a twitch of a curtain which meant Mrs. Warren was peeking out. Bob didn't move.

Tommy was frantic. He raced past Bob and darted into the yard, up to the clump of bushes. Down he flopped and was just wriggling to where he could reach the ball when he heard a door open and Mrs. Warren's shrill voice.

"Get out of here!" she screamed. "Go on! Get out!" He could hear her thumping down the porch steps. Before he could move she had seized the back of his jacket and was dragging him out of the bushes.

"What did you put in those bushes?" her sharp voice demanded. "Answer me! They sent you down, didn't they? Sent you to spy on me, and put bombs in my yard, didn't they?"

Tommy couldn't figure out what she was talking about. Over his shoulder he glimpsed the other boys watching wide-eyed.

"I only wanted to get my ball," he faltered.

"Spying all the time," Mrs. Warren scolded, as if she hadn't heard. "Spying and making trouble. You're the one who's in trouble now. When the police get here I'll — — "

Tommy didn't wait for the rest. Twisting free, he raced to join the other boys as they dashed toward Tommy's house. At last, panting, they reached the safety of the front steps.

"The mean old witch!" stormed Joe. "Somebody ought to get the police after her! Did you get your ball?"

"How could I, with her hanging onto my jacket?" demanded Tommy. "A fine bunch of pals you are, leaving me to argue with her. You could have come up and snatched the ball while she was jawing at me."

Bob and Joe exchanged embarrassed glances.

"I'm sorry," said Joe.

"Me too," Bob said. "All I could think of was getting out of there fast. If I ever get caught in her yard my dad will hit the roof!"

"I don't care!" exploded Tommy. "You threw the ball and you should have gotten it!"

"I didn't throw it in there on purpose!" Bob was beginning to get angry too. "How could I tell where a crazy ball like that would land?"

"Well, when you saw it land there you should have chased it. I'll bet if it had been your ball you'd have gone after it fast enough. But it was mine, so you didn't."

"Oh, yeah?" Bob growled.

"Come on, Bob," Joe said, glancing uncomfortably from one to the other. "We'd better be going."

Tommy watched them disappear down the street. He felt sick with anger. Bad enough losing his ball, he thought, but the two of them had walked out on him as if it didn't even matter. And Joe, who had been Tommy's friend longer than anyone else, had gone right along with them.

"A bunch of double-crossers!" Tommy muttered to himself. "Well, let them go. Good riddance." He walked forlornly out to the pup tent behind the garage where they held their club meetings. Crawling in, he dug out the secret box of club records he, and Joe, and Bob had hidden yesterday. No point in keeping them now. He was through with the club. Let Bob and Joe form their own club. He stuffed the records into his pocket. Opening up the jar of supplies he pulled out a candy bar and began wolfing it down. Might as well eat up the supplies too. By the time his mother called him for supper there were only two candy bars left.

Supper was a silent affair. Tommy was aware of his mother's watchful glances and his father's attempts to make conversation. All during the meal Tommy kept thinking about Mrs. Warren's shrill threats and about how the boys had run out on him. Tomorrow would be Saturday. He saw stretching ahead a long, lonely day, and he didn't like to think of it. Then he remembered that Mrs. Warren had demanded his arrest. Suppose she went to the police! If only he could talk to someone! But the thought of the scolding he would get for having gotten into trouble with Mrs. Warren was too much to bear.

Suddenly the silence was broken by the sound of the side door-bell. Maybe the police were here already!

"Will you see who it is, Tommy?" his mother asked.

Tommy's heart was pounding as he stepped to the side entrance and peered out cautiously. He caught his breath. There, under the light, stood Bob and Joe. What in the world did they want? He opened the door a crack.

"Hey, Tom!" hissed Joe, "What do you think?" His voice was an excited whisper. "Look!"

He motioned to Bob, who held out his hands. He had the ball! Tommy gasped.

"Jumping catfish!" he exclaimed when he caught his breath. "Where did you get it?"

"Sh-h-h!" cautioned Bob. "Boy, did we have a time! We took my flashlight and sneaked up to Mrs. Warren's after it got dark. It was Joe's idea," he added. "His mother wanted him to mail a letter at the corner, so he asked me to go with him. Then we had the idea of getting the flashlight and trying to find the ball."

"Didn't she see you?" asked Tommy anxiously.

"No. She was fussing around in her kitchen. We could see the light. Well, here," Bob added, thrusting the ball at him, "take it. Don't you want it?"

"Boy, do I ever!" breathed Tommy. "Gee, thanks! You're real pals." Then he added, "I sure blew my stack this afternoon. I'm sorry."

"It's all right," Bob said.

"Yeah," said Joe. "Come on. My mother will be wondering what became of us. See you tomorrow." And they were off.

Tommy bounded back into the house and slammed the door. He was grinning.

"It was Joe and Bob," he called to his mother. "They found my ball. I thought I'd lost it."

He hurried up to his room to avoid any questions. Why tell the whole story and get his dad excited? Maybe Mrs. Warren wouldn't call the police. It was just a trick to scare him. He'd been silly to worry about it. Just as he'd been silly to think the boys were against him. Why, they'd even stuck their necks out to get his ball back! Shamefully he remembered the things he'd been thinking and the way he had eaten up the club supplies. Maybe Bob and Joe wouldn't think so much of him if they knew how mad he'd really been. Tomorrow he'd have to put some candy bars back into the supply jar before they found out. He couldn't let them know, not after what they'd done for him.

Suddenly he heard the jangle of the front doorbell. Straining his ears he caught the rumble of a man's voice saying something about "the old lady down the street." Then his father was talking.

"She's a little queer," he was saying, "and imagines lots of things." The voices dropped.

Softly Tommy crept to the head of the stairs and peered down. His heart skipped a beat, for there stood a policeman!

"She says some boys have been spying on her and doing some sort of damage to her property," he was saying. "Your boy was one of them. Two others were around tonight with a flashlight, and she's given me their names — — "

"Dad!" Tommy could hear his own voice as if it were far away and belonged to somebody else. In a sort of daze he stumbled down the stairs into the glare of the hall light. The policeman's eyes swept over him gravely.

"Tom," said his father sternly, "can you tell us what this is all about?"

Tommy was shivering all over. He swallowed hard.

"We didn't do anything wrong," he was trying to keep his voice from trembling. "We were just looking for my ball." He forced himself to look up into the policeman's face. "Please don't go over to the other boys' houses!" he begged. "They were only trying to help me out!"

The policeman's face seemed to thaw a little.

"Listen, son," he said, "suppose you tell us the whole story so that we can get the facts straight. I know boys can get into a lot of trouble over a ball," he added. "I've got a couple of boys of my own."

Little by little the story began to come out; at first haltingly, but gradually the words tumbled out by themselves. Tommy felt good to be talking about it at last. The heavy, frightened feeling inside him was going away.

"Well," the policeman said finally, "you kids do have a problem with Mrs. Warren. There are a lot of queer people like that around. We've got a lady like that in our neighborhood. She's sick you know, only it's her head that is sick. You should feel sorry for her."

"She doesn't feel sorry for us," Tommy said.

"Suppose you really thought everyone who came near your house was going to rob you, or put a bomb in your bushes, or try to kill you. Wouldn't you feel pretty unhappy?"

"I suppose so," Tommy said reluctantly.

"You're lucky in a way," said the policeman. "You can keep away from Mrs. Warren and not have any trouble. But Mrs. Warren can't keep away from herself. Wherever she goes she takes her troubles along, because they're inside her head. Wouldn't that be worse?"

"Yes," said Tommy, "but why doesn't she take her head full of troubles and go some place else?"

"I'm afraid you're stuck with her, Tommy," the policeman said. "The point is, what are you going to do about it? You're pretty mad at her right now. Are you boys going to try to think up some tricks to get even with her?"

Tommy thought for a moment. "That would make her madder than ever. Then she'd suspect us even more."

The policeman smiled. "Good boy, Tommy. You've got it figured out. How about it? Can I give her your promise there'll be no more trips into her yard? For anything? If you get into a spot again, tell your father. Let him handle it. Promise?"

"I promise," Tommy said. He felt tired, but relieved.

When at last he was in bed his eyes refused to close. Dozens of questions were whirling around in his head.

"Dad," he said as his father was opening the window, "can anyone get sick in the head? Even you or me?"

His father nodded. "Yes, lots of people get mentally sick. But lots get well too. Doctors are learning more every day about curing them."

"What makes them get sick?"

"That's a big question," his father answered. "We still don't know very much about the causes of mental illness. But we do know that sometimes people build up ways of thinking that aren't healthy, just as some people build up poor health habits for their bodies."

"What kinds of thinking?"

"One of the worst is being suspicious. You can see what it's done to Mrs. Warren."

"But how can anyone help being suspicious? If you think a person has done something, you think it," Tommy said, "like me this afternoon when I thought Bob and Joe didn't care about losing my ball. I was so mad I never wanted to see them again."

"I know," said his father. 'We just have to learn to stop and remember to look at all the facts. We have to be ready to listen to the other person's explanation. That's very important."

Tommy was silent, but he was thinking. "Suppose you did something mean because you were suspicious," he said. "What should you do about it?"

"What do you think?"

"I guess the best thing," Tommy answered slowly, "would be to come right out and say you were sorry and try to fix things up."

"I guess it would," agreed his father. "I was glad tonight to see you show some good ways of thinking."

"Did I?" Tommy asked, surprised. "You mean when I said I wouldn't try to get even with Mrs. Warren?"

"That's right," said his father. "Carrying grudges can be an unhealthy habit. But the most important thing you did was to tell the whole story about your trouble with Mrs. Warren. Talking about things that worry you is the best mental health habit of all."

"I know," said Tommy. "I feel a lot better now that I've talked about this afternoon. Next time, maybe, I won't wait so long to talk."

"A good idea," said his father giving him a goodnight pat.

Tommy burrowed under the blankets with a tired sigh.

MARGARET RITCHIE

V
The broken family

We Need Our Friends

John broke into a run as he came near his house. He had wondered why Mother sent for him to come right home from school. Now he knew. "Company," he thought, "and a lot of them."

There were three cars parked in the driveway. He gave a big leap up four steps at once and opened the screen door. There were people on the sofa, in the armchairs, even on the piano bench.

He opened his mouth to say something, but before he uttered a sound he suddenly closed it again. He had a funny, sinking feeling. The ladies on the sofa had been crying. Uncle Albert was leaning against the end table with his hand over his face.

Grandma got up from her chair as Aunt Hester, who was sitting nearest the door said, "It's John. You tell him, Mother."

Grandma was crying too. She wiped the tears away as she came to him. But just then John's mother appeared at the door. John felt a little better when he saw her.

"I was hoping you would get here soon. Come upstairs with me. I want to talk with you."

Then Mother told him what had happened. Daddy had had a heart attack at the office. They had called a doctor, but it was too late. He had died before the doctor got there. Some one had called Mother, and she had called Grandpa, and Grandma Lane, and Uncle Albert, and Aunt Hester. Some of the neighbors had heard about it, and they had come in.

Mother went on talking. She explained that everyone wanted to help them, but it was up to her and John to do the planning. Mother sobbed a little as she held him very close. John cried too.

"I'm afraid," John said. "What will we do without Daddy?"

"I know, John," Mother said. "I'm a little afraid too. We will be very lonesome. I guess we'll just have to help each other as much as we can."

There was a tap on the door. "Come in," said Mother.

It was Aunt Hester. "There are four boys at the front door," she said. "They have heard about John's father and have come to tell him they are sorry. Shall I send them home?"

Mother brushed away a tear. "No," she said. "Those are John's friends. At a time like this we need our friends."

"I wonder who they are?" said John.

"Do you feel like seeing them?" Mother asked.

"I think so," John said, "but I don't know what to say to them. I want to do something, not go down and sit with all those grown-ups.

"Why don't you take them into your room and tell them what happened, the way I told you? It helps if you talk about it."

"I don't think I can tell them without crying," he said.

"They won't mind," Mother answered. "Most people cry when something like this happens. It makes you feel better too."

"I want to see them," John said. "Yes, I can talk to them, but not for long because I want to help you."

"Yes, we have a lot to do. But I must go talk to Grandma and Grandpa. They feel as badly as we do, you know. After all, Daddy belonged to them, too."

Aunt Hester invited the boys to come upstairs. They came up. Andy came first, with his hands in his pockets, looking frightened. Then came Jerry, and Walter, and last of all, Gene.

John met them at the top of the stairs. "It's swell of you fellows to come over," he said. "Come in my room."

John tried hard to hold back the tears, but when he tried to tell them about it he did cry. The boys sat looking at him.

"What happened?" they asked.

So John told them about the heart attack. Then he told them how his father had come into this very room this morning to wake him up. He told them every word he had said to Dad, and every word Dad had said to him. Then he told them about breakfast, everything that anyone had said. It all sounded so clearly in his mind now, and he kept talking and talking, and the boys kept listening.

Talking did make him feel better. Some of the things he told them two or three times — he just felt as though he had to talk about it.

Later Mother came to the door, and John said, "I'm glad the

boys came over. It's wonderful to have friends."

"I know," Mother agreed. "I'm glad they are here. I have to go out now and make arrangements for the funeral. Uncle Albert and Aunt Hester are going with me. Grandma and Grandpa will stay here and talk to the people who come to the house. Andy's mother thought perhaps you would like to go over there for supper."

"Would it be all right?" John asked.

"I think it would help you," Mother said. "I have a lot of arrangements to make, and you would be lonesome here. She is calling your mothers too," she said to the boys. "You will all have supper there, and I'll call for you, John, as soon as I get back."

As John walked through the living room Grandma hugged him. She held John very close, and he hugged her for a minute. Then he pulled away. He really wanted to be with his friends now. Tonight he would talk to Mother again, but now he didn't want to talk to all the grownups in the living room. He understood what his mother had meant when she said, "At a time like this, we need our friends."

LUCILE LINDBERG

Will You Play?

Sue was eating her cereal when Mother looked up from the paper and said, "Mrs. William Hamilton. Oh, that's Rachel's mother." She turned to Sue, "Rachel's mother died last night."

"Poor Rachel. Isn't that terrible? She told me yesterday her mother was better, and they thought everything was going to be all right," Sue said. "Rachel was talking about a trip they were planning for next summer."

"She has been sick a long time. It is too bad," Mother said. "I wonder who will take care of the children."

Sue got up and started to put on her coat.

"Where are you going, Sue? You haven't finished your breakfast."

"I don't feel like eating, Mother. Poor Rachel, I keep thinking about her. I'll go tell the other girls." Before her mother had a chance to say anything more, Sue was on her way.

"Hey," she called to Ruth, "Rachel's mother died last night. Mother read it in the paper. They don't know who is going to take care of the children or anything."

"I wonder if they have her body at the house." Ruth said. "When Uncle Lou died they came and took him away to the funeral home."

"Where is the funeral home?"

"I don't know," Ruth answered. "It's downtown somewhere, and has colored windows, and looks like a church."

Just then Genevieve came along. "I called Rachel this morning. Her mother died," she announced.

"We know," replied Sue. "My mother read it in the paper." Then she looked at Genevieve. "You called her on the telephone?"

"Sure, why not?"

"But are you supposed to telephone when someone dies?" Sue said.

"I didn't know she had died."

"How awful," Ruth said. "What happened?"

"Nothing happened. I dialed her number and when someone answered I asked for Rachel."

"And then what did they do?" Sue leaned forward eagerly.

"They told me that her mother had died. But they wanted me to talk to her."

Ruth looked surprised. "Did she come to the telephone? What did she say?"

Genevieve was feeling important. Apparently this was something startling she had done! "She said 'Hello,' and then when she heard my voice we talked."

"What did you talk about?" Sue seemed excited.

"Everything. We talked about Frisky and her kittens, and she told me she had to stay in the house this morning, but this afternoon she would come out and play."

"She isn't! She can't! Surely she isn't going to play! How can she? Her mother died!" Sue was talking very loud.

"She'll get tired of staying in the house. She's lonesome, and she wants to see us. Why shouldn't she?"

"Because, silly, people aren't supposed to play when there has been a death in the family. They are supposed to sit still and — — and — — " Sue hesitated. She didn't quite know what she thought they ought to do.

"She must not have loved her mother very much, or she wouldn't come out to play." Ruth shook her head. She was even a little angry.

"I agree with you," Sue said. "I think it's awful. I don't want her playing with me. Besides, I wouldn't know what to say. Maybe I'd say the wrong thing and make her feel worse."

"I don't see what's so terrible about it," Genevieve said. "I'm going to play with her if she wants me to. She's lonesome. If my mother died, I'd want someone to play with me."

"What will you play?" Ruth asked.

"I don't know," Genevieve answered. "We'll decide that after she comes out. We can play with our dolls or we can work on the playhouse. Why don't you play with us too? That would make it even less lonesome for Rachel."

LUCILE LINDBERG

First Week End of the Month

"Why aren't you going on the cook-out with us?" Alice asked as Roberta came into the meeting.

"Please come," Sue insisted. "We want you. We'll have fun."

"I wish I could, but I can't," Roberta told her. "That's the week end I spend with my father."

Roberta was new in the neighborhood, and what she said about her father surprised the girls.

"With your father? Do you have a father? I thought it was just you, and your mother, and little sister, and that was all," Faith told her.

"I thought your father was dead," Sue exclaimed. "That's what my mother said."

"No, he lives over in Ferndale. Ever since Mommy and Daddy were divorced, I've spent the first week end of every month in Ferndale."

"What do you do when you go over there?" Rose asked.

"We have a good time. Daddy is a big tease. He doesn't scold me like Mommy does. He lets me stay up late and he takes me places."

"What kind of places?" Alice asked.

"The last time I was there he took me for a long drive. We went for a dip in the ocean. He's teaching me how to swim. Then we had hot dogs for lunch. In the afternoon we went to the zoo," Roberta's face beamed as she talked.

"Does he have a house?" Faith asked.

"No, he has an apartment, with a room for me."

"It's too bad your father can't stay at home all the time if he's so much fun," Alice said.

"We think it's better this way," Roberta told her. "He wasn't so much fun when he lived with us. He was worried, and cross, and didn't take me anywhere. He and Mommy argued, and I felt terrible."

"My mother and father argue sometimes. I wonder if they are going to get a divorce? I'd hate it," said Rose.

"Maybe they are," Roberta agreed. "That's how it started with mine."

"I hope not," Rose said. "They only argue once in a while."

"I wish mine would," Alice said. "Then I could have fun with Dad all by myself."

"Daddy says I get by with murder," Roberta told the girls. "If Mommy tells me I can't have something, I ask Daddy, and usually he gets it for me. That's how I got my bicycle."

"Lucky you," Alice told her.

"Sure," Roberta said. "Daddy is going to take me to a circus too. And when I graduate from high school he may give me a trip to Europe. He'd like to take me up in an airplane, but Mommy won't let him."

"You have fun, but all the same I'll bet you wish your father lived with you all the time," Sue said.

"I know it," Roberta sighed. "Sometimes I feel terrible about it. I can't help it, though. The first week end of every month I have to spend with Daddy. That was the agreement when they got the divorce. And Daddy insists on it. It's fun, but it'd be more fun if we could all be together."

LUCILE LINDBERG

Shall We Invite the Fathers?

"We need to make more plans for our play," Miss Patterson said first thing on Monday morning.

"Who is coming?" Pete wanted to know.

"That is one of the things we will have to decide," Miss Patterson told him. "It will depend on when we give it. If we have it in the afternoon, it will have to be for the mothers, unless a few fathers are able to get away from work. If we have it in the evening, we can have both our fathers and our mothers. Let's think this problem through first. What would we gain from each plan?"

Ruth raised her hand at once.

"I think we should have it in the afternoon because the costumes will look prettier. The stage is so dark at night," she said.

"I think we should have it in the evening," Reuben interrupted her. "We can set up some spotlights and the costumes will look nice."

"But it's such a job to do all that work when we could have it in the afternoon without any extra trouble," Ruth told him.

"I want my dad to come," Helen said. "I think it is important for our fathers to know what's happening at school."

"It isn't right when the fathers don't get to see the plays. At our house Mom and I keep talking about little things that happened. This goes on for days. We can't help it — it's very exciting. My father feels left out. I want him to come," Joan was very emphatic.

George agreed with her. "Yes, fathers feel out of things. Dad is going to let me wear his bowler hat and carry his brief case. I think he should see how I look."

"We don't have much room," Ruth reminded them. "If we have both fathers and mothers that will be almost sixty people. How could we get sixty chairs in that room?"

"You are making an important point, Ruth. This has been bothering me. I certainly agree that we should make it possible to invite the fathers if we can, but how can we make all of them comfortable? We will have to solve that," Miss Patterson responded.

Ruth was pleased that Miss Patterson saw her point. So she emphasized it. "We are crowded when our class is in that room. Men and women would take up more room. It would get hot and be terrible."

Bill stood up as he spoke. "We all want to have our fathers and our mothers," he said. "Instead of spending our time arguing, let's plan how we can arrange the chairs. Then we will know."

"Suppose we all think about it and get a fresh start after lunch? We can go downstairs then and try setting up chairs. Maybe that's the only way we can find out whether it can be done," Miss Patterson said. "We'll take our readers now and get to our other work."

Dorothy, Helen, and Pete were walking home for lunch a little later. "I hope we can invite our fathers," Dorothy said.

"So do I," Helen agreed.

"What's the trouble with Ruth? I don't think she wants the fathers. She was the only one who thought it wouldn't work," Pete complained.

"Don't you know!" Dorothy looked surprised.

"Know what?"

"Her father and mother are divorced," Dorothy said.

"You mean her father doesn't live with them?" Pete asked. "Doesn't Ruth ever see him?"

"Not very often. He's married again and lives in Los Angeles," Dorothy answered.

"I don't think it's fair," said Helen, "Just because Ruth's father can't come she doesn't want any fathers to come. That's selfish."

Pete shook his head. "I expect she feels bad about it. That

must be terrible. I wouldn't like it."

"Oh, it's not so bad. My mother has been divorced, but now she is married again, and I have a new father," said Dorothy.

"Then you have two fathers?" Helen asked.

"Yes," she answered, "My own father lives over on Walnut Street. But I think I really like my new father better."

"That must be funny having two fathers," Pete said.

"I don't mind. It must depend on your father and your mother — Ruth seems so upset by it. We talked about it a lot at our house, until we all understood what was going on."

"I think I'd feel like Ruth does if my parents were divorced," Pete declared. "I couldn't give up either of them."

LUCILE LINDBERG

I Don't Understand

"Mary, why are you being so secretive?" Mother snapped as she took the eggs off the stove and put them on the girls' plates. "Take that pencil and paper off the breakfast table. There isn't time for writing now. You'll be late for school as it is if you don't move right along."

Mary stuffed the letter she had been writing into an envelope. She half wished her mother would see it. She laid it on the table and started to eat her breakfast in silence. It was easy to keep from answering her mother's question. The rush of getting off to school was all that really mattered.

On the way out the door she gave her little sister a shove. Janie turned and made a face and then ran on ahead. As Mary ran after her she had a funny feeling that she had forgotten something. The feeling was quickly lost in her effort to catch up with Janie.

At the window Mary's mother watched the girls run off, and then turned to pick up the breakfast dishes. She found the letter Mary had left lying near her plate. In attempting to fit the letter more neatly into its envelope she noticed it was addressed to her sister.

She hesitated, but then she took the letter out and read it. The children so rarely wrote letters unless asked to do it.

Dear Aunt Ruth,
     Daddy is moving away. Mother and Daddy say they are not going to live together any more. Why do they do that? Please, please, please come to see us and tell them not to do it. Mother cries all the time. They didn't tell Janie yet. She's too little I guess. I don't understand about it, Aunt Ruth,
love and kisses and tears and tears,
Your niece,
Mary

Mary's mother sat down at the kitchen table, put her head down on her folded arms, and thought for a very long time. She thought about how unhappy she and Mary's daddy had been this past year. She thought about the things the marriage counselor had tried to help them understand so that they could work out ways of living together without arguing all the time. She thought about the night she and Mary's daddy had decided they could not make the family happy: that they would get a divorce. It had been a hard thing to decide.

As she thought about it all she realized she hadn't done a very good job of helping Mary and Janie understand what was happening. She got up slowly and put Mary's letter back into its envelope. She put the envelope into her pocket and went back to picking up the breakfast dishes.

It seemed to Mary as though the afternoon would never end. She liked arithmetic but she couldn't pay attention to what Mrs. West was saying. She couldn't stop thinking about what she had heard the girls saying in the hall that morning when they hadn't known she was near.

"Did you know Mary's father and mother are getting a divorce? Her father isn't going to live there any more. I wonder if they'll move away? My mother says — — "

But Mary hadn't heard any more. The tears had stung her eyes as she walked away. She had pushed open the door to the girls' room and found a corner to hide in while she tried not to cry. All she could think of was the way they had said that word "divorce." She couldn't understand why her mother had never said that word to her before. The bell had rung and she had hurried to class.

"Why did they think we'd move away?" Mary put her head down on her desk. "The sounded like they didn't like me any more."

Mrs. West had been troubled when she saw the way Mary had been staring out the window, not looking at anyone, not hearing anything. She walked to Mary's desk and said very quietly, "Come with me, Mary."

In the teachers room Mrs. West gave Mary a wet towel to wipe her eyes. "Can I help you, Mary?" she asked. Mary couldn't answer. As Mrs. West talked on, she said things about what a good student Mary was, and how much every one liked her.

Mary blurted out, "But if people talk behind your back they must not like you!"

"Has someone been talking about you?"

"Yes."

"Can you tell me about it?"

"No."

Then Mrs. West said, "Mary, I'll just say this, and then let's go back to class. I know the boys and girls like you, and you really know it too. If someone has been talking about you it is because they don't understand something about you, and not because they don't like you. Maybe you know what it is and can help them understand."

Mrs. West sounded as if she really knew that what she was saying was right. It made Mary feel good even though she wasn't quite sure why. They walked back to class together.

As Mary was walking home from school she remembered the way it had sounded when that girl had said, "Her mother and father are getting a divorce." She felt like shaking the word right out of her head. It made her feel like her father and mother were doing something terrible. She ran up the porch steps and into the house. She nearly ran into her mother, who was coming downstairs from the attic where she had been sorting clothes. When Mary's mother saw the look on her face she reached out her arm and pulled Mary close. Mary buried her head on her mother's dress and cried. Her mother patted her hair. "It's all right, dear. It's all right. We'll find a way to make it better. It's all right."

Then she said, "I haven't been able to talk to anyone these days, not even you girls. Shall we make a fire in the fireplace and just sit and talk?"

Mary looked up. Her mother's voice sounded good. It seemed like a long time since her mother had talked as though it mattered what she said. Janie was playing next door, and for a long time Mary and her mother sat by the warm fire. Mary's father didn't come home very often, and he never came until after dinner.

"Mary," Mother asked, "why did you write to Aunt Ruth without telling me?"

"I guess I didn't think it mattered much to you," she said in a small voice.

"How could you think that?" Mary's mother said quietly.

After a long silence Mary said, "Because you don't talk to me any more. I asked Daddy why he's going away, and he wouldn't answer me. He said he'd see me once in a while to take me to a show or something, but I want him to live here like before."

"Mary, your father and I are not going to live together like before. It has been very hard for us to decide what to do about the way this family should live. I realize now that we have not talked to you carefully about our plans. We have both been unhappy, and have not always known the best things to do. I need you to help me, Mary. We need to make a new kind of family. Your Daddy needs you to understand too. He is going to miss you."

Mary's mother reached over and pulled Mary's head onto her shoulder. Mary felt that good feeling she had when she and her mother were friends. As she listened to her mother talk, she began to feel that things would be all right some day.

EILEEN DAY

What Will the Others Think?

"Joyce! Joyce! I thought you had gone. Hadn't you better start? You don't want to be late the first morning of the new year." Mother held Joyce's coat for her, then handed her her gloves. "Did you bring any books home with you before Christmas?"

Joyce picked up two books and her new pencil box. But she didn't start. "I have a headache," she said. "I think I'm catching cold."

"Let me feel your forehead," said mother. "You don't seem to have any fever. Button your coat up around your neck. You'll feel better by noon. You'd better get started to school."

Joyce closed the apartment door behind her. When she came to the outside entrance she looked both ways. No one she knew was in sight. Maybe if she walked slowly enough she could get to school just when the bell rang and go directly to her seat.

It was only two blocks to school, and when she came around the corner she could see the children on the playground. Sally was standing in the middle of a big group of almost all the girls in Joyce's class.

Just as Joyce reached the door, the bell rang, so she was the first one up the steps and into her room.

"Happy New Year!" Mrs. Renzi smiled at her as she came into the room. "Did you have a good vacation? Aren't those new gloves? They are bright and gay, just right for a sunny day like this."

Joyce didn't feel very gay. She took out her spelling book and made herself very busy writing her words. She kept her eyes on her paper, but she felt as though the girls were staring at her as they came in.

Mrs. Renzi read a poem. Then she asked if anyone had anything he wanted to tell. Hands went up all over the room.

David gave a long involved account of what he did on Christmas day. Joyce found it very dull. Evidently the others in the class did too, because they kept dropping things, and it got so noisy Mrs. Renzi had to call for attention. David always talked too long.

Mrs. Renzi finally stopped him.

"It is time for our arithmetic," she said. "We'll hear from the rest of you later." Everyone got out his book.

A few minutes later Kathy, on her way to the pencil sharpener, laid a note on Joyce's desk. At first Joyce pretended that she didn't see it, but on the way down the aisle again Kathy shoved it to the middle of the desk.

Joyce put it down on her lap and unfolded it. She read it. "Is it true what Sally says, that your father is in the crazy house?"

Joyce fumbled for her handkerchief. Now the tears began to come very fast. She couldn't stop herself. She put her head down on the desk and sobbed.

Mrs. Renzi was beside her in a minute. With her arm across Joyce's shoulder she led her down the hall to the library, which was empty.

"What is it, Joyce? Is it something you can tell me?" Mrs. Renzi asked.

"Daddy had another one of his spells," Joyce began between sobs. "This time the doctor had to take him to the hospital. And all the girls know about it because Sally told them." Joyce broke down and sobbed harder than ever.

"I'm sorry your father is sick," Mrs. Renzi said, "and I know you are worrying about him. What difference does it make if the girls know? I am sure they are sorry. Many people go to the hospital."

Joyce's shoulders shook as she tried to control her sobs. "But it isn't a hospital like other people go to. It's the Midvale State Hospital. My father goes out of his mind when he has a spell, and he doesn't even know us. And they've taken him there to stay for a long time. Sally says he's crazy, but it's not true. It's not, it's not!"

"Tell me more about it, Joyce. It will help you to talk about it."

So Joyce began to talk and tell Mrs. Renzi how it had felt to have the men come and take father to the hospital. She told her teacher how strangely he had acted. She told her how worried Mother had been. Then she said, "I don't really want to talk about it, and the girls will all ask questions. I don't ever want to see them again."

"It seems very hard now, Joyce. But this is something you have to face. The girls will understand, I am sure. Why don't you let me take you to the nurse's office where you can rest for a while? I'll talk to the children, and when they understand they won't ask you questions. After recess you can come back in the room."

Joyce was still sobbing, but not as hard now. It was quiet in the nurse's room when Mrs. Renzi left her there. The nurse was smiling at her, and said, "When you are ready to talk with me, Joyce, you can. Perhaps I can explain some of the things that are bothering you. I worked at the Midvale Hospital once, you know."

LUCILE LINDBERG

VI
Children of different national, racial, or religious backgrounds

Let's Be Friends Anyway

Poochie jumped on the bed to wake up Chuck. "This must be Saturday," thought the sleepy boy, for Poochie was allowed in the bedrooms only on Saturday mornings. After a short romp on the bed with Chuck, Poochie went about his other Saturday business of waking Jimmy.

Chuck started to get dressed. "No school today," he was thinking. "I hope the gang will play basketball at the Catholic playground." Chuck was off in a daydream, imagining himself first as a forward, and then as guard, and then as center. He liked basketball better than anything.

Chuck Baker was eleven, and his brother Jimmy was nine. The two boys liked their school, but it was across town from where they lived, and most of the children in the neighborhood went to the nearby Catholic school. Sometimes this made a problem for Chuck and Jimmy, especially on Saturdays when they all played together.

The Bakers, Chuck, and Jimmy, and Mom, and Dad, lived in a medium-sized house in the oldest part of the city. They wanted to move closer to where Chuck and Jimmy went to school, but they couldn't afford it. The Bakers were just an ordinary family, living in an ordinary house, having ordinary money troubles. They were ordinary people except for one thing: they had some unusual ideas about religion — just downright peculiar ideas according to their neighbors. All the neighbors were Catholics and didn't understand why the Bakers questioned everything!

Chuck was roused from his daydreaming about basketball by Mom's announcement that breakfast was ready, and shortly the family was seated at the kitchen table.

"Why can't we be Catholics, Dad?" asked Jimmy.

"We don't believe the way the Catholics do," answered Dad. "To be Catholics we would have to believe in many things that we don't think are true. How can we do that?"

"I can't," said Chuck.

"I can," said Jimmy. "All I would have to do is say that I

believe. I already know part of the Catholic creed." Jimmy pushed back his chair and stood up and began reciting the creed in a slow, halting voice.

After a few sentences Jimmy sat down and said, "I'll learn the rest from Andy Blair today. Then maybe I can go to confession with him this afternoon."

Mom asked, "Do you want to be a Catholic just so you can go to confession on Saturday with the other boys?"

"Well, yes, sort of," answered Jimmy. "All the kids except us go every Saturday afternoon, and we feel left out."

"Even if we are left out," said Chuck, "I still don't want to be a Catholic. They're so dumb sometimes."

"I want to do just like Andy Blair," said Jimmy, "and he's not dumb either. He's a good basketball player."

"Dumb guys can be good basketball players," said Chuck.

"Andy Blair is not dumb," insisted Jimmy. "He knows all the creeds and the catechism. You don't know those things."

"No, I don't," said Chuck, "and I don't want to either. Even if Andy Blair does know the creeds and the catechism, he is too dumb. The other day he said God could do anything, so then I asked him if God could make a stone so big that he couldn't lift it, and Andy didn't know the answer."

"I'll bet he's found out the answer by now," retorted Jimmy.

"Yeah," answered Chuck, "he probably went and asked the priest."

"Well, the priest knows," said Jimmy. "He knows everything about religion."

Dad broke in on the discussion. "Jimmy, what do you think about Chuck's question? Can God make a stone so big that he can't lift it?"

The doorbell interrupted the conversation. Andy Blair and Tommy Kelly had stopped on their way to the playground.

Mom told them, "Chuck and Jimmy will be there as soon as they finish breakfast."

When Mom got back to the table, Chuck said, "I wish we didn't always have to play on their playground. I wish we lived close to our own school playground."

"I know it's hard to go to a different school," said Mom.

"We don't have to go to a different school," complained Jimmy. "We can be Catholics. Then we can go to their school, and it will be our playground too."

Dad replied, "That might be one way to settle the problem, Jimmy, but you are the only one in the family who wants to be a Catholic. We'll have to think and talk about it a lot longer before we can agree on that plan."

"They only asked us to play with them because we are good basketball players," said Jimmy.

"You do many things with those boys besides play basketball," said Dad, "so there must be other reasons why they like you. People don't have to think and believe alike to be friends. Since you've finished your breakfast, why not go along and show them?"

"And don't forget your mascot, Poochie," added Mom.

Later, after a hard game of basketball, the gang of boys sat down on the grass to rest. They talked about many things, as boys do, and by and by they got around to one of their discussions about religion.

Chuck asked Andy, "Do you know the answer yet to what I asked you last week?"

"What was that?" answered Andy, pretending he didn't know.

"Well, you said God can do anything, so I wanted to know if God can make a stone so big that he can't lift it?"

Andy answered sulkily, "My Dad says for me not to pay any attention to your old questions. He says you're going to hell sure as anything. Aren't you scared?"

"Course not," Chuck replied. "I don't believe there is a hell."

Andy asked, "Where do bad people go then, when they die?"

"No place," said Chuck. "They just die, and that's all."

"Who says so?" retorted Andy.

"My Dad says so."

"Phooey!" said Andy. "Your Dad says so! He isn't anybody. If you had a Pope in your church who said so, then I might believe it. But your Dad! Phooey!"

Tommy Kelly gave his opinion. "Your Dad doesn't know what he is talking about. The Pope says there is a hell, so there must be a hell, and if you don't believe it, you'll go there for sure."

"I don't believe it," said Chuck, and then feeling very sure of himself, he added, "I don't believe there is a heaven either, or a God who sits up in heaven on a throne."

Jimmy hated to get in these arguments with his friends. "Oh, Chuck, for Pete's sake, shut up!" he said. No one paid any attention to him.

"Well, now," said Tommy, "so you don't believe in God either."

Chuck defended himself, "I said I didn't believe there was a God who sat up in heaven on a throne."

"Where does God stay then?" asked Mark, another one of the boys.

"God isn't like a person who has to stay in a certain place," answered Chuck. "I just don't believe there is a God who sits up in heaven on a throne because gravity would make the throne fall down."

Mark accused Chuck, "My Dad says you Bakers are atheists."

"We are not," replied Chuck indignantly. "We just believe differently from you, and in this country people have a right to believe what they want to about God."

"I'll bet," said Tommy, "that you are afraid to run around this church three times shouting that you don't believe in God up in heaven."

"I'll bet that you are too," said Andy, "because you know what would happen if you did? God would send down a bolt of lightning from heaven that would strike you dead on your third time around."

"Oh, phooey!" said Chuck. "Do you think I believe a thing like that?"

"Prove it," shouted the gang.

"I dare you!" said Tommy. "If you don't do it, then we'll know you're really afraid of being struck dead by a bolt of lightning from heaven."

Now the church was next to the school and the playground, and behind the church was a big building where the Catholic sisters lived, and the whole thing was fenced in. Chuck would have to go outside and go around the fence, which was about two blocks on each side. That would make eight blocks altogether, and three times around would make twenty-four blocks, and that would be about two miles. It was a long way to run.

Chuck was thinking about all this. "If I don't go, they will always say I was afraid. But if I do go, I'll feel just plain stupid. I wonder if they really believe that God would shoot down a bolt of lightning and kill me if I don't prove it isn't so to them?"

"Yah, yah, you're afraid!" taunted the boys.

Chuck had made up his mind. "I am *not* afraid," he said, "but I'm not fool enough to run two miles to prove it."

"We dare you! We dare you!"

Chuck stood up and stretched. "We're just different, that's all. Come on Poochie, let's play ball. Anyone else want to play?"

MARJORIE LEAMING

Strange Churches

Bruce hesitated before the stone steps leading to the heavy church doors. A tingle ran up his spine.

"Jim, are you sure it's all right for me to go in?" he asked.

Jim grinned. "Look," he said. "What do you think they do in Catholic churches, anyway? Eat Protestants for breakfast? Nobody minds if you come in. Father Ryan likes to have people visit. You'll just be sitting in a pew while I say confession. What are you so scared of?"

"I'm not scared," Bruce answered. "But you said Catholics aren't supposed to go to Protestant services, so it seems queer they'd let Protestants come to Catholic churches."

"What's queer about it?" demanded Jim. "It's a sin for me to attend a Protestant service, but it's no sin for you to go to a Catholic church, is it?"

Bruce shook his head, still puzzled. Something about it didn't quite fit together, but he didn't have time to figure it out.

"All right," he said, mounting the steps. "Just tell me what to do."

How many times he'd longed to see what went on inside the massive stone church with the gold cross on its steeple! And now that Jim was spending the week end with him the chance had come.

For days they'd been planning the week end program. Jim, whose folks were to be away, would spend Saturday night with Bruce and go on the outing with Bruce's Sunday school class the next morning. It was to be the high spot of the week end. An archeologist from the museum was taking the class to a site where some real Indian graves were being excavated, and Jim was invited along. At first he'd been even more excited than Bruce about the plans. Then suddenly he'd begun to act doubtful.

"You're sure I won't have to go to any kind of Sunday school service?" he'd asked several times after explaining that he wasn't supposed to go to other churches.

"Don't worry," Bruce assured him, though it was hard to see what all the fuss was about. "We'll just meet at Sunday school and pile into cars and take off. There's no sin in that, is there?"

"I guess not," Jim had said with a grin. Nevertheless, it had taken several consultations with Jim's family before everything had been arranged. But at last the plans were completed: Jim would go to confession Saturday afternoon, and then he would go to Bruce's house for supper and to spend the night, and go to Mass early Sunday morning.

"It seems like a lot of church going," Bruce thought to himself as he followed Jim up the flight of steps.

Jim pushed open a set of richly carved doors. Tiptoeing behind, Bruce stopped abruptly to catch his breath at what he saw.

Great columns swept upward and fanned out into sweeping arches which faded into the blue shadows of the domed ceiling. At the far end of the red-carpeted aisle rose an altar of white marble aglow with golden candles, while above, keeping watch over the whole church, hung a giant cross bearing the figure of Jesus. A low railing set off the altar from the rest of the church, as if to make sure no one would touch this special, holy place. Bruce longed to get closer to it, but Jim motioned him to a pew near the back.

Silently Bruce eased himself into the pew and stared.

Bruce recognized one of the statues in the alcoves on either side of the altar. It was Mary. Where her blue robe fell in folds at her feet a row of tiny candles glowed ruby red in the dusk. As Bruce stared her face seemed to come to life. Could she really hear what the woman who knelt before her in the shadows was whispering? Bruce almost expected one of the pale marble hands to reach out and stroke the woman's hair. He had never felt like this before about a statue.

Glancing around the pews he noticed occasional worshippers silently kneeling, their lips moving softly, each one absorbed in some secret thoughts of his own.

A strange excitement stole over Bruce, as if he were peeking through the gates of a forbidden garden. How he would like to come back into the church some time when it was completely deserted!

Just then he felt a hand on his shoulder. Turning, he saw Jim beckon, and reluctantly followed him out.

The spring sunshine struck him sharply. It was hard to believe that things were still the same outdoors. Already Jim had his yo-yo out, and was twirling it expertly.

"Come on!" he was saying. "We'll have to hurry if we want to watch that five-thirty program."

But Bruce couldn't hurry. He was too busy thinking. He hardly knew which questions to ask first.

"Jim," he said slowly, "what were you doing in confession?"

"Talking to Father Ryan. Telling him the sins I'd committed."

"What kind of sins?"

"Oh, all kinds. I called my father a big fat dope. That's a sin. I had a fight with my kid brother. I told a lie to my mother. I said I'd finished my homework and I hadn't. That's one of the worst sins, telling a lie," he added. "That really blackens your soul."

"It does?" Bruce was thoughtful. "I've done things like that, but I never confessed to anybody except to say I was sorry and that I would try not to do them again. How does Father Ryan help?"

"Why he gives you a penance to do so that you'll be forgiven. I've got to say twenty 'Hail Marys,'" Jim explained. "That's a prayer that begins, 'Hail Mary, full of grace, the Lord is with Thee.' I've got to say it twenty times."

"You mean that will really help you stop doing those things?"

"It helps erase the black mark off your soul," Jim said. "There's always a little spot left, just the way there is when you erase something from a piece of paper. But if you don't confess, then your soul gets blacker and blacker. Then when you die you go to hell and burn up forever."

"Do you really believe you will truly burn up?"

"Why sure, really burn up. There are big fires down there and if you die with sins on your soul you'll burn all right, boy. Just wait and see if you don't."

A little shudder ran down Bruce's spine. It was too horrible to be true. Being burned! He thought of the time he'd burned his hand on the toaster.

"But Jim," he said hopefully. "You might be wrong about hell. God's supposed to be good, and that's a pretty awful thing to do. Besides, lots of people don't believe in a real hell like that. Some of them have studied and thought about it a lot. Like my dad — he doesn't believe in hell. Let's ask him about it tonight and see what he says."

"You ask him," Jim said. "Count me out. I know what Father Ryan says, and he's studied plenty — more than your dad — about religion. What he says is good enough for me. I'm not taking any chances."

"Chances!" exclaimed Bruce. "You're not taking chances when you try to find out about something."

"Says who?" demanded Jim. "You're taking plenty of chances. Chances that you'll lose your faith. God gave us the true Church to tell us how to live, and you start fooling around, asking here and asking there, and pretty soon you don't know what to believe. Then you've lost your faith and you go to hell for sure." He thrust his yo-yo back in his pocket.

"Come on!" he said. "Let's get a move on. We'll never get to your place by five-thirty."

The evening turned out to be a huge success. Bruce's mother had just the kind of dinner Jim liked, and he asked for seconds of almost everything. Afterwards the Wharton boys came over and they all played ping-pong and ran the electric train until bedtime. After the lights were out Jim and Bruce told ghost stories until Bruce's father rapped on the door.

Early next morning Jim was up and dressed for eight o'clock Mass. Afterwards he walked back to the house and changed to his hiking clothes so that he and Bruce could be at Sunday school by ten-thirty.

When they arrived a noisy crowd of boys and girls in hiking boots and jackets were milling around the door. Suddenly Mr. Parker, the Sunday school superintendent, summoned them into the chapel.

Jim hung back and touched Bruce's arm.

"What are they going to do?" he whispered.

"Oh, just tell us which cars to ride in. Come on. It will only take a minute."

Jim followed rather doubtfully. He and Bruce sat in one of the back pews. Sunlight streaming through the chapel windows touched the gleaming brass bowl of yellow forsythia on the table up in front. Mrs. Wilde was at the piano playing softly. There was a clean, springlike look to the room. Bruce wondered what Jim thought of it. It must look plain and bare to him after the church he was used to.

The music stopped. Mr. Parker cleared his throat and read the opening words of the service. Bruce caught his breath! Was there going to be a regular worship service? He hadn't planned on this. What would Jim think? Bruce cast a sidelong glance. Jim was sitting rigid and motionless. Bruce couldn't tell what his friend was thinking.

"Because of our field trip, we won't have our regular worship service," Mr. Parker announced. "After our morning offering we will sing one hymn and file out of chapel. At the door you will receive a slip of paper with the number of the car you're to ride in on it. We'll go from chapel directly to the parking lot."

Bruce sighed with relief. As they stood up for the hymn, he shoved the hymn book gently toward Jim. Jim ignored it. He stood stiffly at attention, staring ahead, his lips compressed in a firm, straight line. Bruce felt a little embarrassed singing while Jim stood there like a statue. He began to have a feeling that something was wrong.

It was a relief to file out of chapel. Bruce grabbed Jim's arm and started to hurry him toward the parking lot, but Jim held back.

"I don't think I'd better go with you," he said stiffly. "I've sort of changed my mind. You go ahead, though," he added. "I'll take the bus back to your house and see you there."

Bruce stared open-mouthed. "Why — you'll miss all the fun!" he exclaimed. "What's the matter? I thought you wanted to go! You'll like the kids too — — "

"It's not that," Jim mumbled. "It's just that — well — I don't feel too good. I've got a sort of headache." He turned away.

Bruce didn't know what to do. He wanted to go on the trip, but he couldn't leave Jim. Not when Jim was his guest.

"I'll see if I can get you an aspirin," he said. "That'll fix you up fast."

"I don't want any aspirin," Jim declared. "So long. I'll see you later."

"Wait! I'll come along." Bruce decided it was the only thing he could do.

"No, you won't." Jim looked as stubborn as a mule. "I want to stop off at church first."

Bruce gasped. "But you've been to church once!" he exclaimed.

"Twice," said Jim. "Once to mine and once to yours. I thought you said there wouldn't be a religious service." There was an accusing note in his voice.

"Why, there wasn't!" Shocked understanding began to dawn on Bruce. "All we did was take the collection and sing a hymn. It didn't take ten minutes. You don't call that a service, do you?"

"It's a religious service in my book, whether it took ten minutes or an hour," declared Jim. "I knew I shouldn't have come," he added miserably. He looked almost as if he wanted to cry.

"Oh Jim! I'm sorry! I never dreamed a little thing like that would be a sin. Why we didn't even pray! But anyhow," he added, "it wasn't your fault. You didn't know. Nobody could blame *you*. I'll bet even Father Ryan wouldn't."

Jim gave him a long, slow look.

"Listen," he said, "you're not a Catholic. You just don't understand. In a million years you wouldn't understand. It's okay," he added, "you didn't mean any harm. But I'd feel better if I stopped at church. I'll see you back at the house." He hurried off.

Slowly Bruce turned toward the back entrance. He felt sad and puzzled. He glanced at the worn oak tables in the deserted room, golden brown in the sunlight, and at the familiar doors leading to the supply rooms. It seemed peaceful and open. It didn't have any of the haunting mystery of Jim's church. Yet Jim was afraid. To him it didn't look open and friendly, it seemed threatening.

What was it Jim had said? "You're not a Catholic. You wouldn't understand in a million years."

"But I can try," thought Bruce. "At least it isn't a sin for me to try to find out about things." Perhaps he couldn't understand Jim's church, but Jim couldn't understand his either. To each of them the other's church seemed strange.

MARGARET RITCHIE

The Butterfly Collection

Dave jammed some sandwiches into a paper bag and dashed out to start packing his bicycle basket.

"I'm late for my date with Pete," he called to his mother. "I told him to be at the park by eleven o'clock." He squinted up at the bright sun. "Boy! What a day! We ought to get most of the butterflies we need to finish our collections today."

Mrs. Wilson glanced up and asked, "Do you think your collections will be finished in time for the exhibit?"

"They've just got to be!" Dave said. "Pete's awfully fussy about having every little thing just right. Maybe it's because his dad's a science teacher, but I'm glad. The other kids always get fooling around and pretty soon the collection's a mess."

Dave took his butterfly net apart and laid it carefully in his bicycle basket. "Pete wants me to stop and see his new house on the way back from the park. His folks are settled now. Is it okay?"

"Just where on Westchester Street are they living?' Mrs. Wilson asked thoughtfully.

"Number fifty-two. It belongs to some professor at the university who's going to be away for a year."

"I'm surprised at his renting his place to a Negro family," his mother remarked, "particularly in a section where there aren't any other colored people."

Dave could feel himself beginning to get angry, the way he always did lately when anyone mentioned Pete's being a Negro.

"Well, I can't see what's so queer about it! Pete's folks are as nice as anybody I know! Anyway, they'll only live there a year. As soon as his dad finishes the work he's taking at the university they'll be going back to that Negro college where he teaches. They're not going to hurt anybody's old house living there a year! What's wrong about it?"

"Nothing's wrong, Dave. It's just unusual for a colored family to live in a white section, and sometimes the neighbors don't like it. They shouldn't feel that way, but lots of times they do. I'm sorry I mentioned it and got you upset again. Yes, you may stop at Pete's. But be home by four o'clock. And good luck on your butterfly hunt!"

"Thanks, Mom!" Dave called as he swung onto his bike and wheeled down the driveway. He started pedaling as hard and fast as he could, trying to get rid of the hot, angry feeling. He was sorry he'd gotten angry, and sorry the business about Pete's being a Negro had come up again. It seemed to pop up all the time lately, especially since the two of them had started working on their butterfly collections in the Wilsons' garage.

Dave and Pete had become friends at the Nature Study Club which met at the museum during the summer. Dave hadn't paid much attention to Pete at first, except to notice that his skin was a golden brown, and that he was the tallest boy in the club. He was very quiet and polite, and always said, "Yes, sir," and "No, sir," to Mr. Benson, the club director.

But soon Dave realized that Pete knew more about outdoor things than any of the other boys. His careful way of examining every leaf or insect, the way he was always finding little things outdoors that the others had overlooked, and the questions he asked showed that Pete wanted to learn about everything. Before long he and Dave had started to team up on the club hikes and special projects.

When Mr. Benson announced that there would be a special open house to show people the work they'd been doing in the museum clubs, with prizes for the best exhibits, Dave and Pete had begun working on their butterfly collections almost every day. Pete thought of displaying the butterflies under glass, using old picture frames painted black and gold. It was a wonderful idea, but it meant a lot of work outside club hours. They couldn't do much at Pete's place, because his family was living with his grandmother until Pete's dad could find a house to rent.

So Dave had thought of using their garage. Mr. Wilson had helped them clear out a corner for their work bench and soon they were busy almost every day. Everything went well until the warm day Dave went into the kitchen to get cold drinks to take out.

He heard his mother answering the telephone. It was Bob Gordon's mother, and it sounded as if she were taking the boys to their cousins' place in the country for a swim in their pond.

"Yes, the water ought to be wonderful today," he heard his mother saying. "I know Dave would like to ride out to the farm, but he has a friend visiting him."

Mrs. Gordon said something which Dave couldn't hear.

"Yes, that's the one," his mother said. "He's a fine boy Dave met at the museum. He and Dave are making a butterfly collection. You've probably seen them working in our garage."

There was a little more talk at the other end of the line.

Then his mother said, "Yes, of course I understand, Ethel. Some other time I'm sure Dave would love to go with you. Thank you for calling." She had hung up then.

"Hey, Mom! What was that? A chance to go swimming?" Dave called. "Gee! What's the idea of hanging up without even asking us?"

His mother stuck her head into the kitchen doorway, "Sh! Dave, not so loud," she said quietly. "We'll discuss it after Pete's gone."

Dave started to say something, but he stopped when he saw Pete coming up the back steps.

That evening his mother explained what had happened.

"Mrs. Gordon was very nice about it," she said, "but she explained that she just didn't feel free to take a Negro boy to visit at the farm with her. It's nothing against Pete, but that's the way some people feel about Negroes."

"Well, I think it's a dirty, mean shame!" Dave exploded. "Why Pete's as good as Bob Gordon, or me, or anybody else — better than a lot of kids I know — and smarter! Look how polite he is too. I'll bet he could teach Bob Gordon plenty!"

"Take it easy, Dave," his father had said. "Mrs. Gordon wasn't being mean. Maybe she herself felt all right about Pete, but she couldn't be sure how the people at the farm would feel. You have to remember that some people have been brought up to think Negroes are different, and they can't change their feelings easily. I know it isn't right, but it takes a long time for people to outgrow feelings like that."

"You'll just have to expect people not to include Pete in some things," his mother added.

Dave had been mad clean through. The more he'd thought about it the madder he got. He didn't get over it, either. Like this morning, when his mother mentioned it again, he could feel that same little knot in his stomach.

"Well, one thing about a park," he thought as he pedaled along furiously, "a park belongs to everybody. No Mrs. Gordon or anyone else can keep you from having fun there."

Then suddenly up ahead by the little bridge inside the park he caught a glimpse of a white sport shirt among the trees. Pete rode out from behind some bushes and came to meet Dave.

Pete hopped off his bike and stood with his butterfly net across his shoulder. "Boy, you're late," he remarked. "I've been waiting a half hour."

Dave was surprised. Usually Pete was so busy looking for

insects and things that he never noticed the time.

"I'm sorry, Pete," he said. "Anyhow, there must be lots of butterflies around. Let's hike up the creek."

"All right, let's get going." Pete started walking ahead through the tall grass.

"My mother said I could stop at your place on the way home," Dave said as he swung along behind Pete.

"Okay" was all Pete said. Dave began to get a queer, uneasy feeling. He'd never seen Pete act this way before.

Suddenly there was a flash of orange and black in the tall grass, and a huge monarch butterfly darted up toward some tall bushes.

"Get him, Pete!" Dave yelled. Just at that moment a second monarch fluttered up and off across the open park. Dave took off after it, while Pete chased the first one along the edge of the creek. Dave ran, panting, until suddenly the monarch settled on a tall milkweed stalk. Carefully Dave stole up, his net poised. Quickly he popped it over the butterfly. It was a beauty, all right — big and perfect. Gently carrying the butterfly in the net he headed back to put it in his collecting box.

Then he looked around for Pete, but Pete seemed to have disappeared.

"Hey, Pete!" he called a couple of times. No answer.

Dave gave three short whistles and waited. It was their code call. He gave it again. Finally he heard Pete's answering whistle. It sounded a long way off, so Dave pushed on through the tall grass.

Suddenly he saw Pete. He was lying on his stomach flipping twigs into the water while he chewed on a piece of grass. He'd taken off his shoes and socks and was kicking his bare feet up and down.

"What are you doing?" Dave called.

"Nothing. What does it look like?" Pete didn't even look around. He just kept swinging his feet. The soles of his feet were pink. Dave had expected them to be brown.

Dave flopped down beside him.

"I got a monarch," he said.

"Good, all I got was a couple of wet feet."

"Oh well, the sun will dry your shoes," said Dave. "Anyway, we'll divide our catch when we get back to your place."

Silence again. Dave wondered what to say, then all at once he didn't care what he said.

"Listen, Pete. What's the matter with you anyway?" he burst out. "If you're mad at me why don't you say so and get it over?"

"I'm not mad at you. I'm not mad at anybody."

"Well, you sure act it. What *is* eating you then?"

Another long silence. Pete stopped kicking his feet. He lay very still, looking straight ahead. Finally he spoke.

"We're not sure we'll be staying in our new place," he said slowly. "Maybe we'll be moving back with my grandmother."

"Moving! Why you just got settled. What's the matter? Don't your folks like the place?"

"Sure they like it. But the neighbors just don't like us, that's all."

Dave could feel the knot in his stomach again as his mother's parting words flashed through his mind. But he couldn't let Pete know. Besides, maybe it wasn't true.

"Why that doesn't make any sense!" he said. "Your folks are nice to everybody. I'll bet you're wrong."

"No, I'm not wrong." Pete said it in a quiet, flat voice, "One of the neighbors told my dad last night. He says some of the people on the street are signing a petition, a sort of paper that says they want us to move out. This neighbor, his name is Mr. Ward, wouldn't sign, so he came and told my dad about it."

Dave's eyes blazed. "Well, of all the low-down, mean tricks. Those people must need their heads examined! Why would they do a thing like that?"

Pete suddenly sat up. His dark eyes were angry, but down underneath there was a look as if he wanted to cry.

"Why?" he said. "Why? I'll tell you why! You see this?" He pinched the skin of his bare arm savagely. "Look at that. That's why. You know what's wrong with it? It's the wrong color. It should be white like yours. And there isn't a thing you, or I, or the whole world can do about it!" His voice ended in a sort of dry sob and he buried his head against his folded arms.

Dave couldn't say anything. All he could do was stare at Pete's shoulders and try to choke down the hard tight feeling inside himself.

"I hate them!" The words came spitting out without Dave's even thinking. "Every stupid one of them. Who do they think they are? Your folks are worth the whole bunch of them put together. Listen, Pete, don't let them get you down, do you hear? Can't you do something to fight back?"

Pete raised his head. He stared curiously at Dave.

"My dad's going to try. Mr. Ward's going to try too. Maybe they can keep enough people from signing so that the others will drop the petition. I don't know. I don't care either. I'd rather go back to Grandmother's. They're all Negroes around there. Nobody will think about what color we are."

"Look, Pete, it doesn't make any difference to me, or to the other kids in the club what color you are. I wouldn't care if you were green."

"Maybe *you* think it doesn't make any difference," Pete said, "but boy, it makes plenty of difference to a lot of people." He gave a little laugh, but not as if he were thinking of anything funny.

"I'll tell you the difference it makes," he said. "Do you know that when we drove up here from our other place we had to sleep in the car? You know why? Because we couldn't find a tourist place that would take us. We ate sandwiches we had packed at home. Why? Because we couldn't spend the time to drive around till we found a decent eating place that would serve us. And you say color doesn't make any difference! How'd you like to change skins with me for a while, huh?"

Dave glanced down at his hands. He'd never thought about what color they were. He stuck them in his pockets, out of sight. He could feel a lump rising in his throat, and his eyes smarted. He turned away so that Pete wouldn't see his face.

Suddenly he felt Pete's hand on his shoulder.

"Come on, Dave," he said. "I didn't mean to make you feel bad. You can't help it, and neither can I. My dad says that someday nobody will pay attention to the color of a person's skin. But right now the important thing is to keep proving that a person's color isn't important. Dad says it's the little things we do that will change the way people feel."

"What kind of little things?"

"Oh, being friendly — working together like we do in Nature Study Club — standing up for what's right, like Mr. Ward's doing."

"It doesn't sound like very much," said Dave. "I'd like to poke somebody in the nose."

For a moment they just sat, watching the dragonflies dart along the creek.

Finally Pete said, "Well, I guess we'd better get going and find some butterflies if we want to finish our collections in time for open house." He didn't sound very enthusiastic.

Dave didn't answer. He was busy thinking.

"I've got an idea," he said. "A real good one. What do you say we put our collections together and make one really big one, and enter it under both our names? That way we'd have a really good one."

He watched Pete taking in the idea sort of doubtfully at first. Then suddenly he began to grin. "Say, maybe you've got something. Look at the butterflies we've got that would go together! Like that mourning cloak of mine that you have the mate to. And we've each got a tiger swallowtail, and — — " Pete stopped.

"Oh, Dave," he said. "There's something we forgot — the prizes."

"Well, what about them?"

"Two people can't win the same prize, can they?" demanded Pete. "Besides, we're each supposed to work on our own exhibit. They wouldn't give us a prize for half an exhibit. That wouldn't be fair to the other kids."

"I guess you're right," said Dave.

Pete was silent. Suddenly he faced Dave.

"Look. How badly do you want a prize?"

"I don't know," said Dave. "It's sort of nice. But I'd like to have you get a prize too."

"Same here," said Pete. "After all the work we've done together I'd feel kind of bad if I got a prize and you didn't. And I'd feel bad too, if you got a prize and I didn't."

"Yeah," said David. "You know something?" he went on slowly. "I'd just as soon forget about the prize if you would."

"You mean work on one exhibit like you said?"

"Sure. I'd rather do that, and make a better collection, and have the fun of doing it — to heck with the prizes."

Pete grinned. "That's okay with me. Say!" he added, "We could even include moths if we did it together. I've got a pair of lunas."

Dave scrambled to his feet. "Come on!" he shouted. "Let's quit talking and get busy!"

The next week was filled with feverish activity — frames had to be painted; new labels printed so they were all alike; the butterflies reclassified. Pete's neighbor trouble was forgotten in the rush.

Finally, the night before open house, the last frame was tacked into place and the collection was packed into a big carton for Pete's father to drop off at the museum in the morning.

Promptly at seven the next evening the Wilsons walked up the broad tree-lined walk to the museum. Under the elm trees stretched rows of tables and tall screens on which exhibits were displayed. At the center was a table with two big bowls of punch and piles of cookies. Dave spotted Pete's folks talking with Mr. Benson.

"Come over here and see our exhibit," Pete called. "We've got a special table to ourselves."

They pushed through the crowd toward the Nature Study Club exhibits. Laid out on the tables were collections of stones and leaves, and birds' nests, and insects. But in the center, on a long table covered with a blue cloth, was the butterfly exhibit. Dave stood and stared. The frames, propped up on little easels, glittered gold and black against the blue cloth. Everyone who came by stopped to exclaim over the rows of shimmering insects.

A tall, grey-haired man suddenly made his way toward them. He smiled warmly and shook hands all around as Mr. Benson introduced him as Dr. Warner, the museum director.

"I've been wanting to meet you boys," he said. "That's one of the finest amateur collections we've ever had." We were wondering," he continued, "if you'd let us borrow your collection for a few weeks to display in our junior club rooms. We'd like to show it off to a group of museum people from other cities who will be meeting here in September. You see, we're mighty proud of what you've done."

Dave felt like giving a whoop, and Pete was grinning happily. As they were assuring Dr. Warner that he was welcome to use the exhibit, a man with a flash camera asked them to pose beside the exhibit. They were so excited!

"This is as good as getting a prize," Dave whispered.

"Better," said Pete.

When Dave's father suggested that both families stop for hot dogs together on the way home, the boys agreed everything had been perfect — just perfect.

Next morning, before Dave finished breakfast, Pete was at the door. He came bursting in, waving the newspaper, "What do you think!" he cried. "We're famous! Look!"

Sure enough, there was their picture with Dr. Warner, and a whole story about the evening. They read it eagerly over and over. Every time they came to their own names a little tingle of excitement ran up their spines. It lasted even when they headed for the garage to clean up the mess left from getting ready.

"Was I surprised when I saw the paper!" said Pete.

"Was I surprised last night!" said Dave. "I guess our working together paid off all right."

"Say," said Dave, remembering the day the plan was started. "We've been so busy, what about that petition?"

"Oh, that!" Pete glanced up from the picture frames he was sorting. "We still don't know. Four neighbors have promised not to sign, but we aren't sure the petition will be dropped. I don't care as much as I did."

"You don't?" exclaimed Dave.

"Well, I'm not as mad. Working on the collection helped; and having our pictures together in the paper and all. You know lots of people are working to see that Negroes are treated right. You just don't hear much about it."

"You mean like Mr. Ward and the others that won't sign the petition."

"Sure. And the man who rented us his house. And the people at the museum. And your folks."

"*My* folks?"

"Why sure. Look at their eating with us last night, and letting us use the garage, and helping us — and your mother having me for lunch and things."

"I guess your dad's right about little things being important," Dave said thoughtfully.

Pete looked at him. "Well, you're standing right in the middle of a whole mess of little things that have to be swept up," he said. "How about pushing that broom around? It's too nice a day to spend in the garage."

"Right!" grinned Dave.

MARGARET RITCHIE

The Others Leave Early

"All those who are going to church had better stop work and get their things on," said Miss Brown.

Little shouts of joy went up as the youngsters looked out of the window at the snow. "I bet you wish you were going out with us," whispered Eddie to Cindy.

"Sure, who wouldn't?" answered Cindy, looking longingly out the window.

"Well, serves you right for not believing in God," said Eddie, as he buttoned up his coat.

"What do you mean?" asked Cindy in a shocked voice.

"You said it yourself," answered Eddie. "Remember when I was doing my homework for church and you asked to see it? I was writing out what we believe, and you looked at it and said you didn't believe that."

"I know," answered Cindy, "but that isn't saying I don't believe in God."

"But all I was writing was that I believe in God and His son

Jesus Christ who died on the cross and was raised from the dead," said Eddie.

"But I don't believe in Jesus Christ who died on a cross and was raised from the dead," said Cindy.

"Then you must be Jewish," said Peter, who had come to see why Eddie was so slow.

"No, I'm not," answered Cindy.

"Then why don't you go to religious instruction like the rest of us?" he asked. By this time quite a few children were listening. "Yeah, why don't you leave with those who go to the Protestant church? What kind of a church do you go to? You don't go with the Jewish children, or the Catholics, or the Protestants."

"I go to the Belleville Community Church," answered Cindy. "We don't believe in released time. Even if we did have classes they would be over before Mother could drive me there."

"Why do you have to go to a fancy church way out in Belleville?" asked Patty. "Aren't the churches here good enough for you?"

"Sure, they're good, but we like the one in Belleville better. The people who go there believe like we do."

"Have you been confirmed yet?" asked Nancy.

"Our church doesn't have confirmation," replied Cindy.

"Gosh, almost every religion has confirmation. Even the Jewish people have it," said Fred. "I'm going to be confirmed when I'm older."

"Children, children," said Miss Brown. "It's time to leave."

"Come on Eddie, we'll be late," said Peter. "Besides I want to get out in that snow."

"Too bad you don't believe in something so you could go too," said Eddie.

Cindy watched the children leave the room. The classroom looked so empty now. How she wished Miss Brown would let the four of them who were left go out and play in the snow.

Fred walked away from the window. He started to get a book and then changed his mind and came over to Cindy's desk. "Cindy, what do you do in Sunday school if you don't have to learn anything so you can be confirmed?"

"Oh we do lots of different things. We have discussions, and we take trips, and we study with a microscope," she said.

"You do what?" asked Chris. She had overheard them. "Don't you memorize Bible verses or learn the Apostles' Creed?"

"No, we don't believe in creeds." Cindy was smiling now. These kids were interested, not just making fun of her. The class didn't seem quite so empty.

Miss Brown smiled at them. "Why don't you all draw up your chairs and tell each other about your churches? You seem to be so interested in how each one is different from the other," she said.

JANET GIVENS

I Vote We Keep Maryann!

"Can't I just sit here and say nothing if I want to?" Maryann asked.

Mrs. Brown looked a little cross. "Come Maryann, you heard me. It is time for us to salute the flag. We always do before our meeting. You know that."

"I'll go out and come in later," Maryann said. "I just thought of something I forgot."

Mrs. Brown was firm. "No, Maryann, we will all say our pledge together. Then you may go get what you forgot."

"What's the matter, Maryann? Did you forget the pledge during the summer?" asked one of the girls. "We'll all help you. You knew it best of all last year."

Maryann looked down at the floor. She shuffled her feet and shook her head. She looked as though she were going to cry, but she didn't.

"Come girls," said Mrs. Brown, ignoring Maryann for the moment. "Let's get our meeting started. We don't want to waste the whole afternoon." She began the pledge to the flag, and the girls all said it with her. That is, all but Maryann. She stood there with her head hanging down, and her hands at her sides.

When they had finished Mrs. Brown came over to Maryann and laid her hand firmly on her shoulder. "Maryann," she said. "I don't like this. You deliberately disobeyed me. You know the pledge, and must say it with the others. I can't understand what has gotten into you."

All the girls were looking at Maryann now, and she was clearly upset. Tears were flowing down her cheeks. "I can't," she said. "I can't. My mother won't let me. I guess I shouldn't have come. Maybe she wouldn't have even let me come if she had known where I was going." Then she broke down and sobbed.

The expression on Mrs. Brown's face softened a little now that she knew what was wrong. "Tell us about it, Maryann. Tell us so we can talk about it."

"Mama and Papa joined a new church this summer, one we never went to before. I hate it, I hate it, I hate it! We aren't allowed to salute the flag, not anywhere at all. But I didn't want to join the church. Why couldn't they join and let me alone? Do children have to belong to their parents' church?"

The children gasped a little as Maryann was telling about it. They didn't think it was nice, not saluting the flag. But they had always liked Maryann. They didn't know what to say. They were thinking about not saluting the flag, and about Maryann wanting to, but her parents not letting her.

Bonnie broke the silence first. "I think I sort of know how you feel, Maryann. I've asked the same thing. My folks go to a church, and we have to drive about twelve miles to get there. I'd rather go here in Brownville with my friends. But my parents keep saying that someday I will be glad they took me over there."

Theresa looked a little shocked. "I think children should go to their parents' church," she said. "Our parents are older — they know what is true. I always go with my parents and I am learning what is right to believe. My father would hit the ceiling if I talked like you kids."

"Yes," burst out Maryann, "but they aren't asking you to do things you don't want to do. I don't believe what my parents believe. I want to go back to the nice church we went to last year, but they won't let me. They say they have found it doesn't believe the right things."

"I know," said Bonnie again. "That's what my parents say. I hate our church. It's only got a few children, and it takes so long to go over there. We do have interesting lessons, but I liked the ones at our old church too. I don't think children should have to go where their parents go."

Patsy had been listening, and she had an idea. "Why don't you girls refuse to go next Sunday? Maybe my mother would let me invite you for dinner, and you could go to Sunday school with me. We have a nice one. I don't mind believing what my folks believe. I think they are right."

Mrs. Brown stepped in just then. "Girls, girls," she said, "I don't think you should be talking this way about your parents. You should listen to them. You should go to the church your parents want you to go to. Now let's have our meeting, and stop all this talk."

"But Mrs. Brown," asked Bonnie. "If you think we should do what our parents do, what are you going to do about Maryann? Are you going to let her belong and not salute the flag with the rest of us."

"I will decide about that later," Mrs. Brown said. "I will go and talk with her mother. Perhaps Maryann shouldn't come at all. It is up to her mother to decide."

"That's not fair," said Theresa. "That's punishing Maryann for something she didn't do."

"Theresa," Mrs. Brown looked firm again, "don't talk back to me. I will make the decision and tell you at the next meeting."

"Why can't we all make the decision, Mrs. Brown? Like we do in our room at school," Bonnie was talking fast for fear Mrs. Brown would stop her. "Each of us says what he thinks would be the right thing, and then our teacher lets us think it over. And then we vote. We do what the most people vote for."

"Well, I vote that we all do what our parents and Mrs. Brown want us to do," said Theresa. She smiled at Mrs. Brown. "It will really be better that way. I think it is fair, after all."

"I don't," said Bonnie. "I vote that we should all think for ourselves. If I don't want to go somewhere, I shouldn't have to. If

Maryann *wants* to salute the flag — — "

Just then Maryann burst out crying again. "I don't want you to fight because of me," she said. "I'll just go home. I won't have any friends if I have to go to that old church."

"Now, now girls," Mrs. Brown was firm. "We won't talk about it any more today. Let's all think it over until next week. Talk to your parents about it."

"Sure," said Bonnie, "talk to our parents, so they can tell us to do as they say until we are old enough to decide for ourselves."

"Bonnie," said Mrs. Brown, "stop it! Wait and see what they say."

"But," asked Patsy, "next week can we vote and see if Maryann can still belong? I vote we keep Maryann, even if she doesn't salute the flag."

DOROTHY SPOERL

The Mysterious Neighbors

It was a cold, clear Saturday in late November and the girls on Maple Street were playing porch tag at Shirley's house. The sharp north wind reminded them that winter was on its way, but the Harts' porch was sheltered and sunny. Mary Jane was "it" and was supposed to tag anyone who wasn't touching the porch railing.

Shirley hung onto the railing and glanced over at the big gray house on the corner. A new family had just moved in, and everyone was wondering what they were like. Mary Jane had found out there was a girl in fourth grade.

"My mother was in the school office the day the new girl was registered," she said. "Her name is Rachel Levitsky. Mother says she must be Jewish to have a name like that." It *was* a queer name, Shirley thought. There was something mysterious about having new neighbors with a queer name.

Just then a car drew up in the driveway of the gray house, and people began to get out.

"Look," called Shirley, "there are the new people."

The girls all watched while a man, a woman, and a girl got out of the car. They couldn't tell much about the girl except that she had brown braids and looked rather tall.

"I'll bet they've been to church," said Mary Jane. "They look dressed up."

"Church!" exclaimed Anne. "What would they be going to church today for?"

"Jews go to church on Saturday, silly — at least most of them do," Mary Jane announced. "Only they don't call it church. They call it a synagogue or a temple. I know, because we used to live in a neighborhood where there were lots of Jews. That's why we moved away."

"What's the matter with them?" asked Shirley curiously. She had never heard much about Jews.

"Oh, I don't know. They're just different. They eat funny kinds of food, and they don't celebrate Christmas or Easter. My Mother didn't like it over there. Besides our house wasn't as nice as the one we have now — — Hey!" she said suddenly, nudging Shirley, "You're off the railing. You're 'it.'"

For a moment the girls forgot the new neighbors as Shirley chased them around the porch. Finally she tagged Helen, and Helen tagged Anne, and suddenly Mary Jane was "it" again.

"Come on, I'm tired of this game," said Mary Jane. "Let's play something else."

"That isn't fair! You're 'it'!" everyone said. But Mary Jane stood there, not trying to catch anyone. Suddenly she glanced up at the gray house.

"Look, kids!" she called. "I think the new girl's coming out to play."

They all turned. Sure enough. She was standing in the side yard, dressed in red slacks and a jacket, her brown braids poking out from under a red cap.

"She's looking this way," somebody said.

"I think she's going to come over here," said Mary Jane. Suddenly she had an idea. "Come on," she called. "Let's get out of here!" She dashed down the steps and started racing around the corner of the house toward the Harts' back yard. The others came pounding at her heels.

"Into the playhouse!" yelled Mary Jane. So they all dashed into Shirley's playhouse and slammed the door.

They whispered inside for a moment, and then someone peeked out to see if the new girl was in sight. Every little while one of them would steal out to look and come dashing back to the playhouse to report. It was a little like a game of hide and seek, and rather exciting for a while. But when nothing happened, it began to get tiresome.

"Let's stop playing this and see if she'd like to come over," said Shirley. "I don't think we ought to hide from her so long."

They came out from behind the house, but Rachel was nowhere to be seen. They decided she must have gone inside, because they didn't see her again that afternoon.

That was how the game had begun, the game they had played on Rachel for several weeks now. It hadn't started out to be something they were going to play all the time, but that's how it had turned out.

On school mornings when Mary Jane stopped at Shirley's to walk with her, Mary Jane would pull Shirley back if Rachel was in sight.

"There she goes," she'd say. "Let's wait so she won't see us, and then we won't have to walk with her."

"I don't care if we do have to walk with her," Shirley said. "What if we do?"

"Well, I don't want to. You can go on by yourself and walk with her, if you want to. I'll find someone else to walk with," Mary Jane would answer.

Shirley didn't want that to happen. After all, Mary Jane was her best friend. She didn't want Mary Jane to be angry. And so each morning the same thing happened. And each time it happened Shirley felt a little more uneasy.

She would see Rachel walking along to school looking straight ahead and would wonder what it would be like to have to walk all by yourself and not have anyone to play with. Several times when they'd passed Rachel in her yard Shirley had said hello, but Rachel would answer so quietly one could hardly hear her. She never smiled. She just looked as if she were going to run away and hide. "What makes you think she's queer?" Shirley asked Mary Jane. "She doesn't look queer. She isn't really mysterious. She just looks as though she were afraid."

"Well, I think she's queer. I think anybody's queer who has to go to church on Saturday and eats funny food and doesn't celebrate Christmas. I think that's being good and queer."

Shirley agreed that these things were strange. But she soon forgot about the Levitskys because too many other things were happening. December had come and the days were dark and cold. There was no snow yet, so there wasn't much fun outside. Everyone was thinking about Christmas, which was only three weeks away. Shirley's mother was doing Christmas shopping, and every week several packages arrived on delivery trucks. Shirley tried to guess what they might be.

One Friday afternoon Shirley was supposed to go to Mary Jane's house after school, because Shirley's mother was going down town and wouldn't be back until supper time.

All day heavy gray clouds had hung low above the roof tops, and during the afternoon a freezing rain had been driving against the windowpanes of the school. By the time school was out the rain had stopped, but all the trees and bushes were shimmering with a glaze of ice.

"The bushes look as if they were made out of candy," Shirley exclaimed to Mary Jane as she broke off an icicle and began to suck on it. Everybody was trying to skate on the school walks, but the janitor had sprinkled them with sand.

As the two girls rounded the corner of the block they saw there was no sand on the next street. The sidewalk stretched ahead, a smooth ribbon of shiny ice, perfect for sliding because it sloped down toward Maple Street. Halfway down the street they saw Rachel taking little running steps and then sliding very cautiously as she headed toward home.

"Come on, I'll race you to Maple Street!" called Mary Jane as she gave a running start and braced herself for a long, smooth glide. Shirley followed with two short slides that brought her almost up to Mary Jane. They had nearly caught up to Rachel, and it looked as if they would have to go around her.

Suddenly Shirley heard a lot of shouting and commotion behind her and glanced over her shoulder.

Three older boys, Gary, and Dick, and a boy whose name she didn't know, were laughing and shoving each other around. They seemed to be taking up the whole sidewalk as they chased each other and went skidding down into all sorts of funny positions on the ice.

Suddenly one of them gave a whoop, took a long running start, and came whizzing straight toward Shirley.

"Look out!" she yelled. But it was too late. Before she could get out of the way the big boy in the leather jacket came crashing into her. As her feet shot from under her she shoved Mary Jane, and all three of them went sprawling. The boy was laughing as he got up.

"Why don't you watch where you're going!" spluttered Mary Jane angrily as she got to her feet.

The other two boys were roaring with laughter behind them.

"Yeah, Gary. Why don't you watch out for the girls!" called Dick as he came skidding toward them. The girls jumped aside and yelled a warning to Rachel. Just as she turned he sailed into her, and knocked her off her feet.

"Oh, pardon me!" laughed Dick getting up, and bowing elaborately to Rachel who was trying to make her feet behave so that she could get up again.

Mary Jane slid up to him and faced him furiously.

"Listen, you!" she shouted. "You did that on purpose. I'm going to report you to the safety patrol. You'd better not — — "

But the boys weren't listening. Dick was staggering around pretending to be dizzy. He lurched against Mary Jane and down she went again. Her hat flew off, and Gary grabbed it and started to skate off down the sidewalk with it in his hand while the other two boys cheered.

Rachel, who had finished brushing herself off, glanced up just as he skidded past her. Quick as a flash she reached out and snatched the hat from his hand, then leaped over to the soft, squashy ground bordering the sidewalk and began to run.

"I'll keep it for you, Mary Jane!" she called, as her long legs flashed over the half-frozen grass.

Gary chased after her, but Rachel had gotten a good start and was a fast runner. She managed to keep just ahead of him as Mary Jane and Shirley thumped along behind. The other two boys danced along beside them, laughing and calling out teasing remarks.

Rachel kept on running to the corner, then cut across her yard and plopped down on the porch steps, panting, but still clutching Mary Jane's hat. Gary, who stayed on the sidewalk, had slowed down to a trot. Mary Jane and Shirley raced across the Levitskys' yard and joined Rachel by the steps.

"You just wait!" Mary Jane called. "I'm going to report you. Just see if I don't."

"Oh, yeah? Who are you going to report me to? Santa Claus?" Gary stood on the sidewalk grinning, his feet planted far apart.

"To the school safety patrol, that's who!"

"You and who else?"

"Oh come on, Gary!" called one of the other boys. "Let the baby have her bonnet! We're going down to Dick's."

Just then the door to Rachel's house opened.

"My goodness, what's all the shouting about?" a voice asked.

The girls turned to see Mrs. Levitsky standing in the doorway. She was a plump little woman with a pleasant face and carefully waved grey hair. She was wearing a blue dress.

"Mother, some big boys chased us all the way from school!" Rachel said breathlessly.

"Yes, and they took my hat!" added Mary Jane, "and knocked us down."

Suddenly they were all talking at once, telling Mrs. Levitsky about the boys and what they were going to do to them.

"Wait a minute!" said Mrs. Levitsky. "I can't get a word of this, it's so mixed up. Why don't you come inside to tell me about it. I'll make some cocoa to warm you up."

The girls were suddenly quiet. Shirley looked at Mary Jane.

"Why, I guess it's all right," Mary Jane said slowly, "if I call my mother."

As they trooped into the front hall Rachel handed Mary Jane her hat.

"Gee, thanks," said Mary Jane. "It's lucky you thought to grab it."

By the time they'd gotten their things off and finished telling about their adventure it didn't seem quite so important. Besides, both Shirley and Mary Jane were busy looking at Rachel's house. It looked like a nice house, with silky draperies and polished furniture. They walked carefully across the thick blue dining-room rug, and stared at the long brass candleholder with its row of white candles on the buffet.

The kitchen was large and cheerful, with yellow curtains and a red geranium in the window. From the oven came a warm, spicy smell of something baking.

Mrs. Levitsky seated the girls at the kitchen table and poured cocoa into white cups with little violets on them.

"I have something special I've been promising Rachel I'd make," she said as she bustled around the kitchen. "It's a holiday treat. I think you girls will like it too."

She brought out a plate full of little pastries, and Rachel gave a shriek of delight. The girls helped themselves cautiously, as they weren't quite sure whether they'd like them. But one nibble was enough to make them want more. They thought they'd never tasted anything so good.

"M-m-m," said Mary Jane as she finished the last piece. "It's wonderful. I wish my mother knew how to make it."

"There aren't any really good recipes for it in books," said Mrs. Levitsky. "It's a pastry I learned to make from my mother. Everyone in the European town she came from makes it. We always have it for Hanukkah."

"What's Hanukkah?" asked Shirley.

"Hanukkah is a Jewish holiday which comes in December and lasts for eight days," Mrs. Levitsky explained. "It celebrates a time long ago when the Jews defeated the people who had taken away their temple. A temple is our church, you know. It's a time for parties, and candle lighting, and giving presents. This year Hanukkah begins next Friday."

"It sounds like fun," said Shirley. "A little like Christmas."

"It is fun," said Mrs. Levitsky. "Lots of religions have special winter celebrations, you know — just around the time when the days start getting longer again."

She turned to Rachel then. "Why don't you take your friends up to your room to play for a while?" So they all went up to see Rachel's playroom.

It was a good room to play in because there was linoleum on the floor and they could slide on it in their stocking feet. They didn't have to be careful of the furniture. And there was a dart game all set up. They played darts until everyone had had a chance to win.

Then Rachel brought out a box of old clothes and costumes to dress up in, and they played a game called "statue" that Rachel taught them. It was a little like charades, and when Shirley dressed up like a baby, with a bonnet, and bottle, and an old bath towel for diapers, Mary Jane and Rachel laughed so hard they were rolling on the floor.

They were having so much fun they didn't want to stop when Mrs. Levitsky poked her head in the door to tell them it was five-thirty, the time they had promised to start home.

As the girls finally said their good-bys and stepped out into the darkness they found a surprise awaiting them. A light snow was falling, and already the frozen ground was powdered with white. All up and down Maple Street the street lights glimmered through a gray-white mist of snow. In the houses little golden lights winking through the windows made the trees look like black lace.

"Oh look! It's really winter!" cried Shirley. "Isn't it beautiful?" She stood for a moment and scooped up a handful of snow and tried to make a snowball. But the snow was too powdery.

"I just love winter," she said. "I wonder if by tomorrow the snow will be right for packing snowballs?"

"If it is, I suppose those boys will be pelting us with snowballs all the way to school," Mary Jane remarked.

"They'd better not try it," sniffed Shirley. "Say," she added, "they chased us into a pretty good place today, though, didn't they?

Rachel knows some good games. And I liked her mother, didn't you?"

Mary Jane hesitated, "I guess so," she said.

MARGARET RITCHIE

Why Can't Life Stay Simple?

Jerry, the new boy, was standing by the door as Dick came out of the schoolhouse. The other boys were over by the bicycle racks, talking and clowning as usual. Jerry seemed to want to come over, but he hesitated.

Dick hesitated too. He knew that it was hard to move into a new place and that he really should ask Jerry to join them. Yet he saw Bob, and Harry, and Mike with their heads together. He knew they were making plans and he didn't want to miss anything. He'd speak, he decided, and then go on his way.

"Where're you living?" he asked.

"We're at the corner of Cumberland and Aberdeen," Jerry answered. "We moved in last week, but I didn't leave my old school until Friday."

"Gee, you're only two blocks over from me. That's swell. You'll like the gang," Dick said.

He saw that the boys were turning their bikes around.

Mike looked up. "Are you coming, or aren't you?" he called to Dick.

"We haven't any time to burn," Harry added. There was a strange note in Harry's voice. If Dick intended to go with them he must be off. Jerry looked at him, hoping to be included. But Dick said, "Be seein' you. I have to hustle."

It didn't seem right to leave Jerry standing there, and he didn't like to do it. But Mike and Harry had been ignoring the new boy — maybe he'd better find out why.

He laid his bicycle down in Bob's front yard and joined the others on the steps.

"Thought maybe you weren't coming," Harry began. "What's the matter? Aren't your old friends good enough for you? If you want to get mixed up with him, see if we care, but count yourself out with us. We don't have anything to do with his kind."

"What's the matter with him? We don't even know him. Seems like a nice enough guy. Lives at the corner of Cumberland and Aberdeen, right near all of us."

"Not for me, he's not my kind," said Harry. "You *would* stick up for a Jew. Well, go with him if you want to, but don't come crawling around asking to get back into our gang."

"We don't want anything to do with Jews," said Mike. "You can't trust them. They'd steal the shirt right off your back. You have to watch them every minute."

"They're a bunch of loudmouths too," added Harry.

Dick could feel his neck getting red. He looked at Bob. Bob swallowed uncomfortably, but stopped to tie his shoes and said nothing. Dick decided to try once more. "There are two Jewish families on the street behind us. They don't have any kids our age, but they're nice. They don't steal, and they don't talk loud."

"We're not having any of them on our street," said Mike. "Pop's seeing to that. Everyone on our block agreed that if they sell their house they won't sell it to a Jew."

Dick didn't like this kind of talk. What was wrong with the guys this afternoon? He felt sorry for Bob. Bob didn't dare to speak up.

"Why don't we wait to decide about Jerry until we know him? If we don't like him, we won't need to play with him any more. It will be rough for him with no one to play with," Dick pleaded.

Mike's mother called him and he was off. Bob suddenly decided to go inside.

"Think I'll be shoving off too," Harry said. "What about after dinner? Will you be there?"

"Yes, I'll be there," said Dick.

"Right! Same place. Same time. Same gang." Harry seemed to be warning him.

Dick walked and pushed his bicycle the rest of the way home. He didn't feel like riding. He didn't feel like doing anything. He was hungry, but he didn't even feel like going in the house for a cookie.

Things had looked good this morning. Now they were terrible. All because they had a new boy in the neighborhood. He didn't want to lose out with the gang. They did everything together. Bob's mother took them out to the swimming pool almost every day in the summer. Harry had a neat rumpus room in his basement, and his mother let them roughhouse down there. Mike was full of jokes. He was always thinking of things that were fun to do.

It made Dick mad! What right did Harry have to decide who would be in the gang? Dick didn't like Harry when he got that funny little smile on his face.

And Bob. Why couldn't he stand up for what he believed? But then Dick went on thinking. "Maybe I'd be better off if I didn't say what I think. Why don't I just let Mike and Harry have their way? What's it to me?"

But Dick was miserable. He didn't want to pretend. He wasn't sure that he could. What kind of a gang would it be if he didn't dare say what he thought?

He couldn't pretend he didn't notice Jerry. He had always been friendly with everyone. He wouldn't feel right if there was a boy in the neighborhood with no one to play with.

Dick's mother and dad didn't feel as Mike's parents did about Jews. They always said it was the person who counted. They had taught Dick to believe the same thing.

Dick didn't know what to do. Why couldn't life stay simple?

LUCILE LINDBERG

Mexican or Ball Player?

"Hey, Eddie!" Jim called, running to catch up with his friend. "Wait a minute! Got something to tell you."

Eddie turned and slowed his pace, "Well, I'm listening. Spill it."

"Did you hear the latest? My uncle just broke the news last night. You know, he's on the school board." Both boys were headed toward the baseball diamond on the Jefferson School grounds.

"I know he's on the school board. So what?"

"Well," Jim went on, "it seems that they are sending some kids from Garfield School over to our school this fall."

"What about it?" asked Eddie.

"It's that new law, you know, about segregation. You can't segregate kids in school now. These kids live closer to Jefferson than we do."

"Okay by me," Eddie said. "What's the matter, don't you like the idea?"

"Not so good. Oh, it's all right, I guess. But I liked our class the way it was last year."

"Say," Eddie had an idea, "what about the team? Maybe they'll have some good players."

"That's just the trouble. Who wants those kids on our team? They may even be Negroes and Mexicans — probably are."

"I hadn't thought about that, but what difference does it make? Just as long as they are good ball players."

"Oh, I don't know," Jim didn't seem to like it. "I liked it the way it was last year. We had a good team."

That night after dinner Jim's Uncle William dropped by for a few minutes. Jim turned off the television and decided to listen to him.

"Yes, I expect some families will be upset by the decision of the school board," his uncle was saying. "Now Jefferson will be interracial."

"What does that mean?"

"You know, about a hundred boys and girls are entering Jefferson. They are mostly Negro and Mexican."

"Gee. I don't think that's going to be any good," Jim put in. "I didn't know there would be so many. I don't like it."

"Why not, Jim?" asked his uncle.

"I don't think I'll like those kids. They're different," Jim replied.

"How do you mean different?"

"I don't know, just not like our gang, that's all. They might upset things. I wouldn't care to have them on the ball team."

"Would that be so bad?" asked Jim's father.

Jim did not feel like answering. Why talk about it? He'd see how things were on Monday.

On Monday morning Eddie whistled for Jim and they walked to school together. Several of their friends rode by on bikes and called to them. Then, around the corner came three Negro boys.

"Our new friends are arriving on time," Jim said unpleasantly.

"I wonder if they like coming to a new school," remarked Eddie.

"I wonder how we are going to like having them here," was Jim's reply. "I don't think I like Negroes and Mexicans."

When the bell rang everyone ran to the buildings, and soon the classrooms were all filled. The sixth grade had ten new members from Garfield, six boys and four girls. One of the boys was a Mexican, smaller than the Negro boys. Jim kept watching him, but he didn't smile back when the Mexican smiled at him.

During the morning session the teacher had the class spend a little time getting acquainted with the new people. Ramon, the Mexican boy, had come from Mexico City and had lived in the United States only a year. He spoke very softly, and the class could hardly hear him, and he had an accent. But they learned that he liked baseball and had played in Mexico City. By recess time the class had learned the names of all the newcomers.

Jim thought he might as well find out about the new boy, so he went up to Ramon and asked "You like baseball?"

"Yes. It is a good game," Ramon replied.

"Have you played much?"

"I played in Mexico City," he answered.

"I'm pitcher of the team here," Jim said.

"You are a good pitcher, yes?" Ramon asked.

Jim didn't tell him he was considered the best in school. He just said "I'm pitcher for Jefferson this year." He didn't ask Ramon to play on his team.

After school the boys went out to play on the green field by the playground. The new boys wanted to play and waited around for a chance. Most of them were asked to play in the outfield. Finally the game started, and Jim's side went up to bat.

They made three runs, and now the batter was hard put, with two out and two strikes against him. But when the ball came he hit it far out into right field. Everyone was thinking, "An easy home run," but Ramon, out in right field, was alert. He ran back several yards and was ready. The ball fell exactly where he stood, and he caught it and threw it with ease to the pitcher. A cheer went up from everyone, even the opposing team. When the game was over Jim's team was two runs behind.

Ramon was excited. Maybe now Jim would ask him to play on his team. "Jim, you play well," he said. "I'd like to be on your team next time."

"We'll see if we need you," said Jim.

That night after dinner Uncle William came over again. He found Jim watching a baseball game on television. They watched for a while, then during the commercial Uncle William said, "How did it go today?"

"Okay," said Jim.

"What do you mean, okay? Sounds to me as though you don't think it was okay. How did the Garfielders fit it?"

"There are ten in our class, and one of them is a Mexican."

"What is he like?"

"Oh, he comes from Mexico City and thinks he's a pretty good ball player. He caught a fly today in right field."

"Oh? Well, was he good?"

"Yes, for a Mexican. But catching one fly is no proof. Accidents can happen to anyone. Afterwards he asked to be on my team."

"Well, perhaps you can use another good player."

"Maybe. We don't want Negroes and Mexicans. We got enough without them."

The next day the sixth grade class was reseated, and everyone was really mixed together. The teacher said she hoped now that the old and new people would get acquainted. Ramon was sitting right across from Jim. Ramon looked over and smiled.

It was a whole week before Ramon got a chance to play. Ramon had shown them he could play ball, but they kept going along with Jim because Jim seemed to dislike Ramon so. Then one day Jim was home with a cold and the boys asked Ramon to fill in as pitcher.

Ramon was pleased and took his place on the pitcher's mound. At first he was nervous. Then, little by little, as his confidence grew, he forgot he was a stranger in the school. He played his best. The whole team did better, and at the close of the afternoon Jim's team had won nine to three.

The boys clustered around him afterwards and said such things as: "You're a *real* pitcher, Ramon."

"Ramon, you put them *there*."

"Smooth playing, Ramon."

On the way home from school Eddie stopped to tell Jim about the sensation Ramon had made with his playing.

"Hey, Jim," called Eddie, and whistled his long special note.

The window in Jim's room opened, and Jim stuck his head out.

"What do you want, Eddie?" he called down.

"Nothing much. Just wanted to tell you we've found a good substitute. Thought you might be interested."

"A substitute! You didn't need to do that. I'll be back tomorrow or the next day."

"Well, we had to have somebody today."

"Come on, let's have it. Who was it?" asked Jim, although he knew only too well.

"That Mexican, Ramon. Remember? Only he doesn't seem like a Mexican any more. He's a real guy. You should have seen him fling those curves this afternoon."

The window on the second floor closed with a bang. Eddie stood looking up, wondering. What was the matter with Jim, anyway?

MIRIAM GORTON

Moving Day — Sophiatown

It was summer in Sophiatown, South Africa, but Grace ran down the hot, crowded street to her home. She burst into the front room and threw her book on the table.

"Mother," she called, "Mother!" Her mother walked out from the kitchen.

"Grace, what is the matter?"

Grace stood still, trying to catch her breath. Her black eyes were wide and frightened.

"When are they coming?"

"Here," said Mother, handing her a cloth and paying no attention to the question, "wipe off your face. You shouldn't run so in this heat."

But Grace could tell by Mother's tone that she understood what the question meant. So she started again, "When will they start to tear our house down? Oh Mother, they can't do that."

Her mother sighed. "You've heard them talking. I had hoped you wouldn't have to know for a while."

"Sari's house is torn down. She had to move this morning. We watched them tear down the house next to it right to the ground. Mother, why are they doing it?" Grace wiped her face and handed the cloth back.

Just then a voice called from the next yard, and Mother leaned out the window. "Yes, Uncle, I'll be right there."

"Mother, *when* will we have to move?"

"Don't worry, Grace. We won't have to move right away. I must go help Aunt Mattie now. Her back is lame again. Watch Dannie while I'm gone, please."

Grace hated to see Mother go, but knew she must help Aunt Mattie. Perhaps if I play with the baby I can forget what I've heard, she thought to herself. She picked him up. His face was sticky and smeared with syrup. But he squealed with pleasure when Grace hugged him and clutched at her hair with sticky fingers. Just then Grace's brothers, James, who was eight, and Hugh, who was six, came in hungry and dusty.

She had plenty to do for a while. Grace poured out some water. "Get that dust from your face and hands," she said. "You look as though you had been working in the mines all day."

She splashed some on baby Dannie's face too and wiped it dry. She made sure the boys were clean and that they had dumped the wash water outside. She could see Mother next door but went on working, setting the table for supper. But all the time she kept thinking about how everyone said the houses would be torn down. She couldn't help being frightened.

"Father's home!" James called, as he and Hugh ran to the door.

"See what I found in the field, Father," said James holding out a penknife. Its blade was broken, but it had a shiny yellow handle which Father admired.

"How was school, Grace?" Father asked as he hung his hat up and sat at the table Then he looked at her more closely.

"Why so solemn?" Grace didn't get a chance to answer, as Mother hurried in just then, and they were busy getting supper. The boys talked and argued, and Mother and Father talked about the day's work. Grace was quiet, but no one noticed that she had eaten almost nothing. There just wasn't a chance to talk again — she didn't want the little children to become frightened.

Next morning Grace watched her mother packing some of Father's books in a wooden box.

"Why are white people afraid of us?" she asked suddenly. Mother looked up and frowned.

"Oh, Grace, you must have been listening as we talked last night. Don't let things you hear bother you."

"Father was angry, wasn't he?"

"Listen to me," Mother interrupted, "and try to understand what is going to happen." Mother sat back and began to talk. "This is a white man's city. It is growing, and the white man wants more room. Sophiatown is on the edge of the city, and now it is too close to the white man."

"Then they are afraid?" Grace began.

"Let me finish," said Mother. "Black people live in Sophiatown, and white people don't want to live near black people. So we must move to make room for them, so they can build new houses and factories for white people." Mother's voice was harsh. Grace watched her face and felt even more afraid. She had never seen her mother look like this before. She had seen other people look that way, but not her mother.

"But where — — " Grace started. Her mother went on talking.

"A few miles from here, new houses have been built on the veld. That is where Sari and her family and many others have moved. That is where we will be moved when the time comes."

Mother bent over her packing. The hating look seemed gone, but she looked very sad.

"I hate white people!" Grace burst out suddenly. "Why can't they build their factories and their big houses out on the veld? Why can't Father tell them we aren't going to move. I hate them."

"You mustn't ever say that, Gracie," said Mother firmly. "You know he can't. We black people aren't allowed to stand up to the whites. There are many things even your father can't do. Some day you will understand it better."

Mother had said that before — she had said it often. Grace remembered a morning when she was standing by the fence outside a city park. She was watching a group of white children playing inside. They were playing catch, and one of them reached too far and fell. The others laughed, and so did Grace. When one of the girls saw Grace she told her to go away. She picked up a handful of sand and threw it at Grace. The other children picked up sand too, and Grace shouted back. But before Grace could throw the pebbles she had in her hand her mother grabbed her and hurried her away.

Mother was very firm that day. "If a white person does or says anything you don't like, pretend it doesn't matter. And run away as fast as you can," she said. "You *must* do this."

"But the sand hit me, and they called me a dirty Kaffir," Grace had said angrily.

"Don't let them know that it matters. You'll understand why

some day."

Grace still didn't know whether she understood or not. But now she asked again, "Does Father have to pretend that what a white man does doesn't matter?"

"Go and see what Dannie is doing," said Mother, not answering the question.

Grace went out and found Dannie sitting watching his brothers play ball.

"Hi, Grace," Hugh called. "Did you know we are going to move? They are going to take us away in trucks and tear down our houses." His voice was excited. "Mark says his big brother and some of his friends are going to kill the first white man who tries — — "

"You stop that talk!" A voice thundered from the next porch. Grace saw Uncle scowling down at them. "Don't let me ever hear you talk like that again!" The small boys scattered, and the street was almost empty except for a few hens that were scratching in the hot dust.

One morning a week later Grace woke up earlier than usual. It was still dark, and she could hear rain falling on the tin roof. The sound of voices came in from outside, and she looked out. Grace could see lights in the house next door. She saw a crowd of people out by the street, some standing, others hurrying, and all with bundles on their heads or in their hands. James's and Hugh's cots were empty, and Mother hurried in.

"Get into your clothes — then help me pack," said Mother. "We haven't much time." Mother stripped the blankets from the cot and rolled them into a big bundle. She looked angry again, as she had when Grace asked her about the moving.

"We aren't moving today, Mother? We aren't," Grace was pleading, as though it would make a difference.

Mother only said, "Get dressed, Grace." She turned and tied Dannie to her back to keep him from pulling things out of the packed baskets.

Grace pulled on her dress and hurried outside. James and Hugh were on the porch. Father, Grandfather, and Uncle Dan were piling things onto the large truck that was parked in front of their house. The furniture was piled so high, and there was so much on the truck already that Grace wondered where they would all ride.

Hugh clutched Grace's skirt. He was frightened and almost whimpering. Grace felt pretty frightened herself.

"What are those soldiers doing? They all have guns." His eyes grew round. "Are they going to shoot?"

"They aren't soldiers. They're policemen," James said. "I asked Grandfather. He says they are here to see that everyone moves quietly — that no one stays behind. I wonder what would happen if someone refused to move. I — — "

"Hush, James," said Grace. "You talk too loud." She looked at the policemen. Some were white, and some were black, but they all had stern faces. She shivered and looked back at the people who were packing.

"Come, let's carry some things down to the truck," Grace said. Hugh dragged the blanket roll to the edge of the steps. Grace went in to pack the rest of her things and found her mother already pushing them into the baskets.

"Did you remember my hairbrush?" Grace asked, poking through the basket. Nothing else was lying around, so she carried it out.

The motor of their truck was already running, and Grace saw the trucks at the far end of the street starting to move. Aunt Mattie was already seated. She hugged a large teakettle in her lap. Suddenly Grace remembered she hadn't said good-by to her friends and started to run down the street. But her uncle reached out and caught her and swung her onto the truck.

"Now is no time to run off," he said. The driver sounded the horn and shouted impatiently. James and Hugh climbed up the side like monkeys and landed on a mattress. Uncle Dan climbed up and, breathing heavily, settled himself. No one said anything much.

Grace watched the house anxiously. She wished her mother and father would get on too. At last they came out. Their home looked bare and ugly now. Father closed the front door and he and Mother walked down the steps. Father's face was dark and angry. Mother's face was blank, as though nothing could matter. Grace had that strange frightened feeling again.

The driver made the engine roar, and Father boosted Mother up. Then Father climbed on. Grace could see that he was trembling. She knew he must be feeling very angry, and there was nothing he could say or do.

The trucks moved down the street in a long slow line. They passed empty houses and yards that were littered with papers, cans, bottles, and boxes. They passed small neat houses, sagging houses, iron shacks, lean-to's made of boxes, homes where people were still living, and places that were already torn down.

They passed hundreds of people who stared at the trucks with their piles of furniture and people. Then they moved out of Sophiatown. Grace began to feel wet and cold in the rain, and she saw that James and Hugh were shivering. They just stared at everything without speaking. Grace poked James.

"Say something! Your eyes are so big they'll fall out."

"I'm hungry," said Hugh. Large tears rolled down his cheeks. Dannie whimpered, and Mother stuffed a piece of bread into his mouth. She gave everyone a slice of bread from the loaf she had in her basket. Grace bit into her slice remembering that they hadn't had any breakfast.

Soon they could look back and see the tall gray buildings of the city. Around them were the smooth flat dumps from the gold mines, yellow and white even on a rainy day. Sophiatown was becoming a mass of gray and black in the distance. Now they were going through another town with buildings close together and crowded streets. It was like Sophiatown.

"We are going through Orlando now," said Father.

"My teacher lives here," Grace said. She began to wonder what their new home would be like.

Just then Father said, "We are almost there." Grace and the boys jumped up to look. Father pointed out Meadowlands to them. They looked at the new town and saw hundreds of houses with shiny roofs, all built in straight rows, and all looking alike.

"How will we know which is ours?" Hugh gasped.

"If we go out how will we know which one to come back to?" James wanted to know.

Grace tried to cheer them up. "We could paint our door red," she said, trying to laugh.

"And then everybody else would like our door and paint theirs red too," said James.

"Then we'd be lost again." The little boys cheered up as they talked and laughed a little. But none of the older people smiled at all.

Soon the truck stopped in front of one of the houses, and they began to unload. It didn't take long for the yard to be covered with chairs, tables, and bundles, and the truck clattered off. Grace followed her mother into the house. It was clean and smelled of wet cement.

"Well, anyway it's clean," Mother said. The men moved things in, and Mother and Aunt Mattie decided where they should go. Soon all the space was filled. By night everything was in its place.

It was chilly out in Meadowlands, and they sat around the stove. There were many things to talk about. Father had learned there was a bus that would take him to work. He would have a long walk to the first bus stop and would have to start earlier. Mother would have to look for a new job. The family she had worked for wanted their cook to live nearer than she was now.

"Where will I go to school?" Grace asked.

"We'll have to wait and see. There will be time enough to find out."

Grace waited. Then she asked what she had been wondering about all day. "Will they let us stay here?" she said. "Will they? Or will the towns grow and — — "

"Sh-h!" said Father firmly. "We mustn't talk about it. We must try to forget about it. Don't let me hear you talking about it again."

Grace lay awake after she had gone to bed. It was the same cot she had waked up in this morning, but the room was new. The smells of the house and the outdoor sounds were strange. Only the smell of her blanket seemed familiar — it had the smoky smell of Sophiatown.

She began to think about her friends and wondered if she would see them again. She wondered if their old house had been torn down. She wondered what Sophiatown would be like when the white people began living there. And again she wondered what would happen if the city grew so big that the white people needed more room. Where would the black people in Meadowlands be moved? She was still wondering when she fell asleep.

ESTHER BAILEY

Two Dinky Rooms

"Why can't we go to church like everyone else does?" asked John, who was sprawled across the living room floor reading the Sunday paper.

"What did you say? Why don't we go to church? We do go to church. I've been asking you to get ready for the last half hour. What *are* you talking about, John Martin?" his mother inquired.

"I mean, why can't we go to the same kind of church the rest of the guys go to? It's stupid to drive all the way to Rayport. There's a church across the street, a church around the corner, a church over by the schoolhouse. So what does this silly family do? Do we go to any of these churches? Oh, no. Not us! We go twenty miles! How crazy can you get?"

"And for what?" he continued. "What do we have when we get there? A bunch of dumb kids in a couple of dinky rooms up over a store! Now I ask you, what kind of a church is that?"

John dragged himself out of the room, not waiting for an answer. He knew better than to stall any longer. Mom would get emphatic about it any minute and make him put on his good clothes. Since there was no way of avoiding it, he'd rather go before he was forced.

He put on his gray suit. It wasn't his newest one, but he hoped that if he wore this one he wouldn't have to change when he came home. He knew exactly how things would be. The fellows would be gathered over on the Bells' front walk. Maybe if he had on this suit Mom would let him jump out of the car and join them. If he had on the new blue one, he could hear her say, "John, you know you must change your clothes before you go to play. Put on your jeans. They'll take the hard knocks."

Then he would argue that he would be very careful, and he surely would change after dinner. But Mom would win and he would waste time changing. In this gray suit there was a chance — a slim one.

John didn't like it. He was always the last one of the gang to get home. The others didn't have so far to come. Bert had to go the farthest. His synagogue was ten blocks away. But he, John Martin, had to come twenty miles — twenty miles!

He was still grumbling as he slid into the car. He did get to sit with Dad in the front seat. He preferred that to sitting in the back seat with Ruth and Janet. Most of the time Mom was a good sport about it and said, "Let's let the men sit in the front seat this morning."

"What are you grumbling about, John?" his mother asked. "You don't seem to be in much of a mood for our drive. Let's cheer up so we can have a pleasant ride. It's a wonderful morning."

But John was still feeling put out, and his mother's attempt to get him to forget it made him even more disgusted.

"What difference does it make what kind of a morning it is when we have to spend it in two dinky rooms — two dinky rooms up over a grocery store," he complained.

"What's all the trouble, son?" Dad asked.

"He's been complaining all morning because we don't go to a church in the neighborhood," explained Mother.

"We'll get a church of our own out here one of these days, but just now we feel lucky to have found this little fellowship," said Father.

"I hope the guys never find out that we don't even have a church building like they do — two dinky rooms." John was almost growling.

"Come now, John. How you do exaggerate. Those rooms aren't so small," interrupted Mother. "The largest must be eighty feet long."

"Jim's father says we are heathens. He thinks it's too bad because we seem to be such nice people otherwise," observed John.

"I suppose it is hard for our neighbors to understand why we don't go along with them on their beliefs," Father commented.

"Well, why can't we?" John wanted to know.

"We want to attend a church where we can think in our own way. We want to have a religion in keeping with all the new scientific discoveries," his dad told him.

"Sure, of course we do. But everyone wants that — we don't have to go out of town to get it," John retorted.

"That's just it. We really do. I used to go to another church, and they thought I wasn't very religious because I questioned so many things," Dad said.

"We ask questions all the time," John told the family. "This morning we are going to talk some more about how the world was made."

Mother smiled. "You have a good time when you finally get there, don't you, John? I saw all of you standing with Mr. Smith around the globe last Sunday. You were having such an exciting discussion that I wanted to join you."

"It was good. We do have fun," he said sheepishly, "but I could have that in any church."

"In some churches you are supposed to accept things on faith," Father said. "You would be considered impudent if you asked so many questions."

"You mean, just believe what they told you to believe without knowing the reason? I couldn't do that," John announced.

"No, I don't think you could," Mother agreed. "I hope not, anyway. We want you to think answers out for yourself. We like to do it ourselves. That's why we go to this fellowship church, just so we can be with other people who feel the same way about these things. We were very happy when this group organized, and we are willing to drive twenty miles. It seems worthwhile to us to be with people who understand our way of thinking."

"When I get there, I like it," John admitted again. "I guess I don't like to get moving so early on Sunday morning. And another thing, I do feel foolish because none of the guys understand why we don't go to the churches right in our own town."

LUCILE LINDBERG

VII
Issues stemming from the adult community that affect the child

She Doesn't Speak a Word of English!

"Mrs. Andrews! Mrs. Andrews! Did you hear?" Bill came rushing into the classroom, out of breath from running up the stairs.

"Good morning, Bill," greeted Mrs. Andrews. "What big news brings you rushing in before the bell rings?"

"I was just down in the office and I heard it all! We're getting a new girl in our class. She just came here from Italy and she can't speak a word of English. Someone who can speak both English and Italian is filling out some cards for her in the office right now!"

As Bill was talking the bell rang, and the other boys and girls came into the room. Bill repeated parts of the story to some of them, and an enthusiastic whispering began to spread through the room as the boys and girls hung up their coats and sat down at their desks.

"Who's going to teach her how to speak English?" asked Christine.

"How will she know what to do? None of us can speak Italian!" added Greg.

"And there's so much to learn when you come into a new school," David reminded them. "I remember when I came to this school last year! If she can't understand English, boy, is she going to have a hard time!

"Can you remember what was so hard, David?" Mrs. Andrews asked.

"Oh, I didn't know any of the kid's names, or where anything was, and things like that. I didn't even want to come back to school the next day."

"Well, we could tell her our names and show her where things are. You don't have to say anything for that — you can just point," suggested Linda.

"Yeah, show her things like the pencil sharpener and the girls' room," added Bonnie. "We could smile to show her we are glad to have her in our room.

"That would help," said David. "But there's something about a new school that makes you almost want to cry the first few days."

"Say, I have an idea," interrupted Greg. "Why couldn't we get her started by teaching her a few English words like 'hello' and 'good-bye.'"

An enthusiastic response sounded through the room. "Gee, we could all be her teacher," said Maria.

The children began suggesting some other words, such as "pencil" and "paper," and Mrs. Andrews wrote them on the blackboard. Suddenly a hush swept the room. The principal was standing at the door with a small, dark-haired girl. He introduced "Rosa" to the class, and said something to Mrs. Andrews. When the principal left the room, Mrs. Andrews turned and saw the class all smiling as they had said they would. Rosa was smiling a little, and Mrs. Andrews introduced her to Susan who showed her around the room and pointed to the desk Mrs. Andrews had said would be Rosa's. Before the day was over several children had a chance to show Rosa something and teach her how to say it in English.

The next day Mrs. Andrews suggested that the children let Rosa teach them Italian words for the objects they were showing her while they taught her the English words.

"Buon giorno," said Joanne when she saw Maria the next day.

"Arivederla," said David as he left in the afternoon.

"I guess we'll soon be speaking two languages," commented Linda one day.

A few days later a notice came from the principal, and Mrs. Andrews read it to the class:

> This Friday there will be a special assembly. Mrs. Thomas, a parent in our school, will talk to us and show slides she took on her trip to Europe this summer. All the classes are invited.

The children talked eagerly about the assembly. Some told stories they had read about countries in Europe. Some told things they had learned from their fathers and mothers. Friday just couldn't come soon enough.

But Friday did come, finally, and Mrs. Andrews' class was seated in the auditorium. The lights went out, and Mrs. Thomas flashed a picture of a boat on the big screen and started talking.

Everyone was quiet except for some "ooh's" and "ah's" and an occasional laugh. Then Mrs. Thomas started to show some pictures she had taken in Italy. Suddenly Rosa started to talk right out loud!

No one could understand what she was saying, nor could anyone make her understand that she shouldn't talk right now. Finally the principal put the lights on, and everyone was looking at Mrs. Andrews' class and Rosa.

"Does someone have a question?" the principal asked.

Once again Rosa blurted out something, mostly in Italian with a word or two of English. No one could understand. The children were embarrassed to have everyone looking at them, and Mrs. Andrews pulled Rosa down into her seat and gently put her hand over Rosa's mouth.

But Mrs. Thomas spoke to the teacher from the platform. "Perhaps the little Italian girl recognizes the place." Then she said a few words to Rosa in Italian, and Rosa beamed. Then Mrs. Thomas spoke to the whole group in English, "That was a picture of the town where Rosa lived. No wonder she was so excited."

Rosa kept looking excited and happy, but she did not try to talk again.

A few days later Rosa happened to be absent, and the children started talking about her in class.

"I hope she's gone back to spaghetti land," said Greg, and laughed.

"That's not a nice thing to say," commented Christine.

"I don't care," scowled Greg. "It was fun having her here in the beginning, but it's getting boring now. She doesn't remember all the words we teach her, and she doesn't even seem to want to learn new ones. And look what she did to us in front of the whole school at the assembly. I think she's dumb. I wish she weren't in our room anymore."

"I told my mother about her," added Beverly. "She says we shouldn't pay any attention to her. She says all the people in Rosa's country are like that."

Mrs. Andrews thought for a moment and said, "Let me ask you this. How many of you can tell me all the Italian words that

Rosa has taught you?"

"Not me!" some shouted. No one said he could.

"But Mrs. Andrews," interrupted Greg. "That's not fair. Rosa's language has all those funny *r*'s in it. We don't have them in ours, so English is easier to learn."

"Oh Greg," said Christine, "our *r*'s are just as hard for Rosa to learn. Ours only seem easier because we've always said them. How would you like it if I kept repeating words in Italian to you and got mad when you didn't remember them?"

"I wouldn't like you any more," confessed Linda.

Several boys and girls nodded in agreement. "I guess Rosa feels the same way we would feel in her country," said Jack. "It's just that she is so different. I know how Greg feels. I don't really like having her in our class much either."

"Neither do I," said Pat.

Mrs. Andrews looked at her class. They were all beginning to nod their heads and agree!

JANET GIVENS

That Polish Costume

"Mama, Mama, are you home?" Helenka Polunsky burst through the kitchen door and threw her books on the table. "Mama, Mama," she continued to call as she ran through the house.

"Ah, you make so much noise, Helenka. Come, sit in here and talk to me nice." Mrs. Polunsky had stopped her embroidering to look at her daughter, who was standing in the doorway.

"Mama, Mama," Helenka said, "guess what? We are going to have a Halloween party at school and we are all coming in costumes. Mary Jane suggested it would be fun if we all came in Spaceman suits with those funny glass bubbles over our heads. Then Miss Miller would think she was teaching on Mars or something."

Helenka giggled a little whenever she thought of her teacher standing in front of a class of Spacemen!

"Please, Mama, could we go to Fishmen's Department Store this afternoon and get a costume before they are all gone?"

Mrs. Polunsky stared at her with deep blue eyes that suddenly seemed to be very bright. "No, Helenka, I no like this Spaceman suit business. You are a pretty little girl, not a man. A glass bubble on your head? No, I no like this for my girl."

Helenka looked at her mother and tried to speak, but the words just didn't come out. Her cheeks flamed and her eyes filled with tears. Her mother wasn't going to let her have a Spaceman suit? She just had to have one!

"But Mama," she finally blurted out, "*everybody* in the class is going to have Spacemen suits on. Everybody — the boys and the girls. I'll be the only one who doesn't have one!"

Mrs. Polunsky looked at her daughter again. Her eyes softened as she said, "Let me make you look nice again, Helenka, like I did when you were a little girl. Remember? I'll get out the nice costume I used to wear when we had parties in Poland. A nice skirt with pretty colors, and a nice blouse with big sleeves I made myself. And I'll buy you new ribbons for your braids. Then you will look like a nice little Polish girl, not a Spaceman."

Helenka buried her head in the arm of the chair and cried loudly. She couldn't stop and she didn't want to. She didn't care if the whole world heard her.

"Helenka, Helenka, stop that crying!" Mrs. Polunsky was standing next to her daughter and shaking her.

After a while she stopped a little to cry out between sobs, "No, no, I won't wear that Polish costume. I won't go to the party. I don't ever want to go to school again." Helenka tore herself away from her mother and ran into her room. She flung herself on the bed and began to cry again.

She must have cried herself to sleep, for when she raised her head from the bed it was just beginning to get dark. Good smells of simmering meat poured out of the kitchen and reminded her it was supper time. Quickly she got up and ran into the kitchen to set the table.

Helenka stopped when she reached the door. The table was set for two because her father was working tonight. Mother was standing at the stove. She didn't turn around as Helenka spoke. "I guess I fell asleep, Mama."

Helenka waited, and then repeated, "I said, I guess I fell asleep."

Mrs. Polunsky turned with a pot in her hand and walked to the table where she began to put the food on the dishes. Helenka pulled out her chair and quietly sat down. Still Mrs. Polunsky didn't speak.

Helenka tried to think of something to say. Finally she tasted some food and said, "Ummm, this is delicious."

Mrs. Polunsky glanced at her daughter again. Her eyes. were burning. "You like good Polish cooking, but you are ashamed to look like a nice Polish girl."

Helenka dropped her fork. Her hand twitched, and her eyes blinked. "But Mama, I'll be the only one. I'll spoil it for the whole class. Please Mama, please let me have a Spaceman suit!"

Mrs. Polunsky shook her head. "No, I don't want to see my girl in a Spaceman suit. That's ugly. I'll make you look so pretty — just like I used to look when I went to school."

Helenka didn't say any more. She was afraid that if she spoke she would tell her mother how much she was hating her this minute. Anyway she couldn't speak. She had to use all her strength just to swallow the food that seemed to stick in her throat.

Mrs. Polunsky didn't say any more either. After they had both finished eating, she started to wash the dishes. Helenka automatically picked up the towel and started to dry them and put them away. What a lot of noise they seemed to make tonight.

"Helenka, I want you to come with me now." Mrs. Polunsky wiped off the top of the sink and turned off the light. She walked in front of Helenka and led the way to her bedroom. Quickly she took the top off an old trunk that was standing in the corner.

"Look, here it is. It still has the hem I put in it for you in kindergarten. Go put it on. Remember how nice you looked?"

Helenka took the clothing from her mother. She held it up

against herself as she looked in the mirror.

"It looks pretty now, but wait until I have washed it, and ironed it, and fixed it so it fits you again. Remember how the blouse sleeves looked like two beautiful balloons? How pretty you looked! And I will teach you a dance to do when you wear it, so you go round and round. Then everybody can see how beautiful you look."

Helenka folded the blouse and skirt and left them on her mother's bed. She went to her own room again and sat in a chair and stared out of the window.

As she watched the leaves swirl in circles and then scatter, she thought again about the party and the costume her mother wanted her to wear. No, she couldn't wear it! No one would talk to her again! They would call her "Helenka the Pole" for the rest of her life. Maybe they would even laugh at her when she said the pledge of allegiance to the flag! No, no!

All of a sudden she was aware of some noise in the kitchen. Her mother was running the water. Helenka heard her singing as she washed and rinsed the blouse and skirt. If only she could get a Spaceman suit to wear under the clothes her mother was going to make her wear, so she could take them off before she went into the classroom. Then her mother wouldn't be mad at her, and she wouldn't spoil the fun for the rest of the class.

She tried to think of some way to get a Spaceman suit. She couldn't make one, that was certain. Maybe someone in the fifth grade had one they would lend her. She didn't know anyone who had one, though.

Helenka began to feel frightened again. She couldn't think what to do next. There didn't seem to be anyone who could help her. She couldn't talk to teacher, because she wasn't supposed to know about the Spacemen suits. And the kids in the class would laugh at her if she told them. She just knew they would!

Slowly she took off her clothes and got ready for bed. Suddenly she felt how cold the room was and hurried to snuggle under the blankets. She lay still for a long time. It was quiet and warm in bed. No one was angry and no one laughed at her.

Helenka could hear her mother in the kitchen. She must be hanging the clothes up now. She remembered the last time her mother had washed them for her to wear in kindergarten. She had been happy about it then. Her teacher had made her go to all the rooms so that everyone could see her.

But now it was so different! Now it wasn't just a dress-up party. Now it was a special fourth grade Spaceman-suit party, and her mother wouldn't understand. What would the other children think? She could hear them laughing already. That Polish costume! Why did her mother make her wear it?

The moon shone through the window, and she could see the chair with her clothes on it. She looked at her heavy stockings and big brown shoes, and began to cry softly again. It would have been so nice to look like everyone else for the Halloween party.

JANET GIVENS

His Brother is a Coward

Joe walked along the street whistling happily. This was a good place his folks had moved to. He'd already met a half-dozen kids who were going to be fine to play with. Maybe soon he'd have a chance to show them what a good ball player he was.

At the corner he saw a boy he hadn't met sitting on the steps. "Looks nice," thought Joe to himself. "And, oh boy, see that tennis court out back!" He decided he'd like to know this boy.

"Hi," he said.

The other boy answered, but without much enthusiasm.

"My name's Joe," said Joe. "I'm new here. Live just around the corner."

"I know," said the boy.

Joe was getting discouraged, but it *was* a good tennis court. He decided to try again.

"You play tennis?" he asked. "Next to baseball it's my favorite game. We played a lot in the town I came from."

"I used to play," said the boy. "You *want* to play?"

"Sure," answered Joe. "What's your name?"

"Dave."

Dave and Joe played a couple of sets. Dave was a fine player, but he didn't talk much. They were starting the third set when the boys Joe had met in the morning came along. They stopped and looked, but they didn't say anything.

"Hi," called Joe. But no one answered. Joe wondered what was wrong. Dave sure looked unhappy.

"Hey, Joe, come here a minute," called Bill.

"'Scuse me a sec," said Joe.

"You playing with that coward?" Bill was sort of nasty.

"He's a good tennis player, but a quiet fellow. Doesn't act like a coward."

"He is, though," said Bill, and the other boys crowded close. Joe noticed that Dave was putting things away.

"Hey, wait, Dave, I'm coming back," he called.

"Go back if you want to — — "

"Say, what's eating you guys?"

"Oh, tell him, Bill," said Ned.

Bill looked at Joe. Bill seemed determined to make an impression. "He's a coward — his whole family are cowards. Why — —," he stopped a minute to show how important what he was going to say was, "his brother is in jail for being a coward!"

"Traitor too," said someone else. "My dad says they're probably Communists."

Joe was puzzled. This didn't make sense to him. "Gee, I just can't believe it. Whoever heard of putting people in jail for being cowards?"

"You calling me a liar?" Bill came closer.

"Sure," said the others. "Dave's brother's in jail all right. Our folks don't want us playing with jailbirds."

"Dave," called Ted. But Dave had already gone in.

Joe stood a minute and shook his head. "They just don't put people in jail for being cowards. You know it."

Bill glared at him. "They don't, don't they? Why he wouldn't even register for the draft. That's why they put him in. Whole family says war is wrong. They won't fight, or buy bonds, or anything."

"Oh," said Joe. "I know. They must be Quakers. We had a lot of them where I came from. They aren't afraid to fight — they believe it's wrong. My mother says it takes real courage to stand up for what you believe if it's unpopular."

Bill sneered. "So you're a coward too. One coward always finds another, right away."

Joe spoke quickly. "No, I don't agree with them. My big brother is in the Coast Guard now. I'll choose the Marines. I just said ideas like that don't — — "

"We heard you," Bill said. "You play with whomever you want to. Okay by us. We just thought this morning you seemed to be a good guy."

Bill started to walk away, with the others following. Ted stayed behind and said quietly, "Good for you, speaking up. I wish I dared. Say, you know, with you and me and Dave there'd be three of us — — "

"Coming?" bellowed Bill.

"See you tonight," Ted said, then louder, so Bill would hear, "Think it over, Joe. You can be lonesome when you play with the wrong guys."

Joe was confused. Everything had happened so quickly. Bill **and his friends** had turned into the park. He knew he ought to follow them if he wanted to play ball on their team. He looked over at the court, but Dave was nowhere in sight. He felt sorry for Dave. No wonder he didn't have much to say. Still — —

"Gee," he said to himself, "how does a guy decide? Ted and Dave seem like swell boys, but anyone can tell that Bill runs things. I've got to be careful."

As he walked along he remembered a discussion they had had in church school last year. He could almost hear himself — he had said, "At least if someone decides what he believes, I'd stand up for his right to believe it."

He could almost hear what his teacher had answered too. "You know, Joe," she had said, "it's easy to say what we'd do. But sometimes it takes real courage to do what we believe. Don't be too sure you would be that brave until you have shown yourself you can do it."

"Gee," he said, sort of talking to himself again, "here I am, faced with it, and I don't know what I *am* going to do."

DOROTHY SPOERL

What Will Happen to Us?

Sally leaned over the railing of the bridge and watched the white foam on the yellow water moving below.

"Do you think the river will get to look like any other river after the mill has closed down?" she asked. Janet joined her at the rail.

"Gee, no. It's always been like this. Grandfather says he's never seen it any other way."

"Well, I think it will. My father says it's the chemicals that get dumped into the river that make it this way," said Sally.

"Then why did you ask?" Janet said impatiently. "Anyway, who cares what happens to the river? I just care about what's going to happen to us." She paused. "My dad says we're going to move soon — to a place where he can find a good job."

"Oh no!" Sally looked at her friend dismayed. "You can't move too. Janice is moving, and so is Patsy. It's going to be terrible with all of you gone. Can't your father find a job right here?"

"Are you kidding?" Janet laughed. "In this town?" She kicked at a nail that had come loose from one of the bridge boards. "This is a moldy town. Dad says he should have left it long ago, before the mill had to close. It's backward, decaying, and there isn't a thing here for people who want to live decently."

"You don't mean that, and you know it, Janet Hancock," Sally said angrily. "You just say that because you have to move."

Sally swallowed, trying to keep back the tears which had suddenly come into her eyes. A worry that had started that morning came back. "We'll never move. Not even if we are the only people left in town," she finished.

Janet looked at her. "I guess your father would never find another job anyway, would he?" she asked more kindly.

Sally turned on her. "What makes you say that?" she demanded.

"I was with you in the store when they were talking about him this morning. Don't you remember?"

Just then a car started over the bridge and the cables shook with its weight. It slowed down as it neared the two girls, and Janet's father called from the window.

"Aren't you going to ride home with me?" he asked. As Janet climbed in beside him he turned to Sally. "Don't you want to come as far as your house?"

Sally shook her head, "No, thank you." She watched the car disappear around the bend and started walking slowly up the road.

The small white house was hidden from the road by a clump of trees and bushes, but Sally could see smoke rising from the chimney. The room felt pleasantly warm when she got inside. Mom was sitting by the table feeding the baby. She smiled when she saw Sally.

"I'm glad you're home."

"I meant to hurry, Mom, really I did. But Janet and I were talking and I didn't realize we talked so long." She took the baby's hand and started to play with her. "Where are Dad and Brian. Hunting again?"

"Yes, and they are going to be hungry when they get back, so I'll let you finish feeding the baby while I get supper for the rest of us."

Sally took the spoon and started to give the baby her cereal. She went on talking to Mom while she fed the baby.

"Janet's moving. Her father has to find a job somewhere else." She laid the spoon down. "Everybody's moving, Mom, just because of that old mill. We won't, will we?"

"I doubt it. The house is all we have."

"Mom, why did they let Dad work in the mill here, if they wouldn't hire him anywhere else?"

"What makes you ask that?" Mom kept on with what she was doing, but she frowned and her voice was sharp.

Sally hesitated, but saw that her mother was waiting for an answer.

"Janet and I were in Taylor's store before school this morning. They were talking about the mill — you know, the way everybody does now, and wondering what was going to happen to the town and the people. Then I heard Dad's name. I couldn't hear what they said very clearly, until Mr. Taylor said that no one would hire a cripple. He said that they only kept him on at the mill because he had worked there so long. Then someone said that he felt sorry for you and the children, and a woman said she always wondered how we lived, even when Dad was working, and she didn't know what would happen, and — — "

The baby began to fuss. Sally picked up the spoon again and fed her the rest of the cereal.

"Will we be poor, Mom? I mean really poor, like — — "

Just then the door burst open, and Sally's brother, Brian, came in carrying a dead rabbit by the ears.

"Hi! See what we have for you, Mom," he said proudly. Then he turned to Sally, "Something for you to skin, Sis." He walked toward her, teasingly swinging the small animal backwards and forwards as he neared her.

"Take that thing outside!" Sally shrieked.

"Brian, stop teasing your sister," Dad said good-humoredly from the doorway. He moved across the room and sat down heavily in a chair.

"Take the rabbit outside," he added, propping his cane up against the wall. "Well, what happened today to make you look so sober?" Dad asked Sally, smiling.

Sally wiped the baby's mouth carefully with the bib and put her down on the floor to play. She didn't say anything.

"Sally has been hearing talk about the mill," Mom explained.

"Oh, that. Don't believe everything you hear. You know how people talk."

"But, Dad, Mr. Taylor said no one would hire you. And the people in the store wondered what was going to happen to us," Sally interrupted.

Dad took his pipe from his pocket, filled, and lit it. "I'm not so sure about no one hiring me," he finally said, quietly. "But I might be out of work for a long time."

"Then we'll be poor?"

"You must be used to that by now," Dad's face was stern.

"But will we be awfully poor, and have to wear other people's old clothes, and — — and — — " Sally felt so much like crying that she could hardly breathe.

"Sally, go outside and tell Brian to come in and wash up for supper," Mom said.

Sally found Brian by the side of the house. He was skinning the rabbit, but she didn't care. She sat down beside him, and he looked up grinning. Then he frowned.

"Say, what's the matter with you?"

Sally took a deep breath. "Nothing," was all she said.

"Then what are you sniffling about?"

"Do you think we'll be anything like the Rickses?" Sally didn't wait for an answer. "Suppose Dad never finds another job. You know what happened to Mr. Ricks."

"Dad's not Mr. Ricks."

"But Mr. Ricks lost his job at the mill years ago, and they're all so poor." Sally's voice grew shrill. "They're dirty, and mean, and spiteful, and Mom said it was from being so poor. Remember? She said that feeling hungry, and cold, and worried most of the time made them that way." She blew her nose on the hanky that Brian handed to her.

"I don't want to be that way," she sobbed. "I want everything to be the way it was before the mill decided to close down, and nobody was scared about what was going to happen."

Just then the door opened, and Mom's voice called out, "Sally, Brian, time to come in now."

ESTHER BAILEY

The Strike

"David, wake up!"

David burrowed further down under the covers.

"Get up, you'll be late for school." The voice was louder this time.

David opened his eyes and saw his father, dressed in his working clothes. He sat up quickly. "Is the strike over, Dad? Are you going back to work?"

"No," David's father shook his head, smiling at David's eager questions. "No, it's just my turn to walk on the picket line, but we are having another meeting this afternoon. We might reach an agreement then." Dad seemed hopeful today.

But David felt out of sorts as he walked to school. He didn't feel like hurrying. He went by the factory and looked for the picket line. They must have been at the other entrance because he didn't see anyone. It seemed funny that the office people, whom he could see through the window, weren't on strike too. Dad had said it was because they didn't belong to his union. There were a lot of things David found hard to understand about the strike: Why did it last so long? What was it really all about? What did the picket line do?

He was beginning to get very tired of the strike, anyway, because of the things that happened at home. All week, ever since the strike had begun, Dad had come home cross from meetings. It seemed as though Dad and Mom scolded more. Mom had even scolded him for being slow this morning. He had quarreled with his sister more than usual. What was wrong with everybody?

Then he had a thought that cheered him. Tonight he and Sally would get their allowances, and tomorrow was Saturday. David walked faster and got to school just in time to miss being marked down as tardy.

This morning, instead of the usual social studies lesson, Miss James talked about labor unions and the growth of the labor movement. The class talked about the strike, and since several members of the class had fathers who were striking or were officials in the factory, they knew something about the details. David felt proud as Miss James described some of the improvements in working conditions, working hours, and wages that unions had helped to bring about. His father was one of the men who had helped start the union in his factory. The morning went quickly, and David was surprised when the bell rang for recess.

After school David and Paul walked home together. Paul said, "How about coming over tonight? We can play in my gym if we want to."

"I can't," said David. "Dad makes us do our homework on Friday night to get it out of the way. But I can come over tomorrow."

"Okay," Paul answered as he went along past David's house, "see you in the morning."

Friday nights at David's house seemed special to him, even with the homework to do. Dad came home with his paycheck on Friday, and Dad and Mom joked about all the things they would do with it. David and Sally got their allowance on Friday night too. Then after supper the whole family sat around the table and talked about things. It made David feel very grown up.

Somehow tonight wasn't the same as other Fridays, though. Mom and Dad didn't joke about the paycheck because Dad didn't bring one home. Sally and David got their allowances, but only half the usual amount.

"I can't do anything with this," Sally said, looking at the money. "I need —— "

"You'll have to learn to manage with that much, at least until the strike is over," Dad interrupted.

"But it isn't fair," Sally complained. "Why should we have our allowance cut because you wanted to go out on that silly strike!"

"Sally!" David looked at his older sister with shocked surprise. "The strike is important."

"What's so important about it? All that's happened has been a whole lot of meetings where union members argue with the company about getting more pay. Then the company says they can't afford to pay more. So they all go home and come back the next day to argue some more."

"That's not the whole story," Dad said, "nor is it quite as useless as you have made it seem."

"Why don't you meet together and still go on working?"

"What do you think all those meetings were about before the strike was called?" Dad asked impatiently. "For weeks I have been working with the other members of the negotiating committee trying to show the management that we can't afford to work for our present wages. It was only when there was no other way left that the strike was called."

"But what if they really can't afford to pay you more?"

"They can't afford not to," Dad said. He sounded very sure, but David felt confused.

"I still don't understand," Sally insisted. "You need more money, so you sit around for weeks without any pay at all!"

"It does sound confusing," Mom said. "All the reasons for the strike and all the details about it are difficult even for adults to understand. This time your father and the other workers are striking for higher wages because the cost of living has gone up, but there are other reasons for calling a strike. Sometimes it is because working conditions are poor or even dangerous, or the working hours might be too long. The strike sometimes can force the company to improve a lot of different things."

Dad spoke now, and he spoke quietly, as he always did when he was very serious. "Sally, if you knew more about history you would see how important the strike is. It's not so long ago that things were very different. In 1817 it was considered very revolutionary when Robert Owen suggested that the children of factory workers be taught to read and write. And one of the new things in his factory which was considered to be a model factory, was that no children below the age of ten should work! You need to stop and think how much things have been improved. Then you would see that strikes are important."

David felt very important that he knew things Sally didn't know. "Yes," he said, "in social studies we learned how strikes have shortened the working day and made factories take care of people who got hurt working there, and how people now get paid after they retire. Just think, people used to work their whole lives and then just get fired when they were old."

Sally shrugged her shoulders and yawned. She didn't seem particularly interested.

Mom looked at the clock.

"We'd better stop talking," she said, "so you can get your homework done before you go to bed. Upstairs, now, both of you, and get at it."

David called down from the top of the stairs, "Wake me up early, will you Mom? I'm going over to play with Paul."

The next morning David was out early and went right over to Paul's. Paul's mother opened the door. "Good morning," she said. "Come in and wait. Paul is just finishing his breakfast."

"Hi, I'm almost through," Paul said.

Paul's father turned to David. "How did yesterday's meeting at the factory come out?" he asked.

"They didn't decide on anything," David answered glumly.

"Were you ever in a strike, Dad?" Paul asked.

"No, we've always been able to get what we needed without having to strike," Mr. Evans said. "A few years ago I doubt if we could have, though."

"Why?"

"I think they have learned from what has happened in other places that it doesn't pay not to be fair. Our company has played it smart and given us things before we asked for them."

"I wish they would do that at Dad's factory," David said.

"Things were pretty bad at your father's factory before they got the union organized," Mr. Evans said.

"How do you know?" David was surprised.

"I used to work there," he said. "Unions help to bring about changes and improvements. But I wouldn't like to see them get too much power."

"Why?"

"Dad," Paul said before his father had a chance to answer David's question. "David came over to play. Let's not talk about the strike."

So the boys ran out to the barn. Paul started climbing one of the ropes, and David took the one next to it.

"I'll reach the top first," he said.

Just then they heard a voice ask, "Can I come in?" It was Frank, a boy in their class at school, who lived nearby.

"Sure, come ahead," Paul said as he slid down to the floor.

"Your mother said you were out here," Frank explained. He looked around.

"This is quite a gym," he said and ran to the bars. He pulled himself up to the top bar, turned a quick somersault and landed upright on the ground again.

"How do you do that?" Paul and David exclaimed together.

"It's easy. I can do a lot more. You want me to show you?"

It didn't take them long to learn, and then Frank showed them some tricks on the ropes. When they got tired they sprawled out on the mattress to rest.

"Where did you learn all those things?" David asked.

"At the community house where we lived last year," Frank answered. "They had everything there — swimming, basketball courts, a gym." He looked at them to make sure they were impressed. "We used to have swell times. I was sorry when we moved to this dumb town."

"Why did you move?" asked Paul, yawning and turning over.

"The place where my Dad worked had a strike. It went on for weeks, so Dad got fed up and quit. He had to come to another town to look for work."

David sat up. "He shouldn't have quit," he said indignantly.

"Why not?" Frank answered. "It's his life."

"Because he defeats the purpose of the strike if he does that," David answered. "He should have stayed and seen it through with the others."

Frank snorted. "You get that out of a book or something?" he asked. "I suppose he should have stayed and let us all starve to death!"

David was about to answer, but Paul spoke quickly.

"Where does your father work now?"

"Same place his father works," Frank pointed at David, and then added, "and if this strike lasts much longer he's going to walk out on it too. You know something? The union leaders tricked everybody into striking. My dad says the vote wasn't fair, and he's going to make sure there isn't any union the next place he works!"

"I suppose he'd take the pay raise, though," David said. "That is if he hasn't run out by then."

Frank ignored David's interruption. "The union here is just a racket," he went on. "All the leaders are a bunch of loud-mouthed trouble makers." He started to walk away, but David grabbed him, and Paul looked uncomfortable.

"Take that back!" David said, shaking Frank.

"Cut that out, you two," Paul said. "Dad said if there was any fighting I couldn't have anyone in here to play." He tried to push the two boys apart, tripped, and found himself sprawled on the floor with David and Frank on top of him.

"Stop it!" he howled as he felt a fist come down on his chest. He was as angry now as the other two, and he struck out at both of them with his hands and his feet. Suddenly they both sat back on their heels and stopped.

"Gee, you two are stupid," Paul said. "If you say anything more about the strike I won't let you use my gym again. Not ever!" He walked over to the ropes and started swinging.

"What's a strike got to do with us, anyway?" he said. "We can't do anything about it."

ESTHER BAILEY

Night in Town

The worried feeling began to harden into a tight ball of fear as Kenny glanced again at the clock outlined against the dark blue neon lights across the street. Nine-thirty! What in the world had happened to Mrs. Kennedy?

Since twenty minutes of nine he'd been waiting in the North Street entrance of Jackson's Department Store, expecting to hear a horn and see her red station wagon glide to the curb. Gradually the evening shoppers had thinned, and the store lights dimmed, one by one. Now he stood by the blackened entrance watching the auto headlights stream past, knowing it was hopeless. She wasn't coming.

Usually on Friday nights either his father or Bill's father picked them up at the downtown Y after swimming class. But tonight Bill was home with a cold. How he wished Bill were here with him! Mrs. Kennedy had offered to pick him up after her hair appointment, since she lived next door. He had come over here so it wouldn't be out of her way. Could she have forgotten? He wished he were at least waiting at the Y instead of here on a corner in the chill November wind!

He couldn't even get a bus. That was the trouble where they lived — no bus service. Glancing at the darkened windows he decided he had better call home. He hadn't dared to do so before for fear Mrs. Kennedy would come while he was calling. He saw a light glowing in a little store where the word "Tobacco" blinked in red neon lights.

The place was stuffy and murky. Kenny glanced around. The long, dark counter was deserted, but at the rear a sliver of light showed beneath a curtained doorway, and he could hear men's voices. The curtain was suddenly poked aside, and a man appeared followed by a boy in black dungarees.

"So long, Tony," the boy said pushing past the man. "Be seeing you!"

Kenny's heart bounced; he knew that voice! "Hi, Joe!" he said.

The boy stopped. "Well, Kenny, the trumpet player!" he said. "You still going to orchestra Saturday mornings over at school?"

Kenny nodded. "What happened to you? We're short of trombones since you quit."

Joe shrugged. "I got too busy. I'm selling papers and working in a grocery on Saturdays. I was on a music scholarship, and they take it away from you if you haven't time to keep up your practice. Say," he asked curiously, "how come you're hanging around Tony's?"

Kenny explained his problem. "I've got to call and see if my dad or somebody can pick me up. I'm really stuck," he concluded. Joe considered a moment.

"I'd wait here with you," he said, "only I've got to pick up some beer for my old man. You want to come back to my place and wait? It's just a dump," he said apologetically, "but it keeps the wind off. It's right near here."

"Gee, that would be great!" Anything was better than standing around downtown. "Just wait while I call home. What's your address?"

After getting instructions from Joe he telephoned. It seemed good to hear his mother's voice. She sounded both relieved and worried.

"I can't imagine what happened to Mrs. Kennedy," she said. "I'll try to reach your father. If I can't, I'll find someone else to run in and get you. You say this boy was in the junior orchestra? Just what is his address?"

When Kenny told her, she paused. "I think that's a pretty poor section," she said worriedly. "Maybe you'd better wait right there by Jackson's."

"Oh Mom! I don't want to hang around alone downtown any more. It might be another hour."

"All right, Ken," his mother answered. "Go straight to that boy's house and stay there. I'll try to reach your father."

"All set?" asked Joe, who had been flipping through a comic book. "Come on, then. We'll stop at Nick's for the beer and beat it over to my place."

They turned down a darkened alley and scuffled along. "Where do you have your paper route?" Kenny asked, mostly to make conversation.

"I don't deliver papers. I peddle them on the corner of North and Andrews from four-thirty to seven at night."

"Jeepers! No wonder you don't have time to practice!" said Kenny. "That's too bad. You were a smooth trombone player."

"Thanks," Joe sighed. "We did have a lot of fun, didn't we? Remember that concert when Bill flubbed his french-horn part and got us all loused up on the 'Hallelujah Chorus'?" Joe chuckled.

"Poor Mr. Wade, standing there waving his baton at all that squawk. I thought he'd pass out! I wish I could have kept on," he added, "but you don't make money that way. Boy, do I need the dough! Anyhow, I got this jacket from selling papers."

Kenny thought of the fleece-lined jacket his father had bought him for his birthday. "Where does your dad work?" he asked.

Joe snorted. "Nowhere right now," he said, "except playing the numbers. He's been out of a job for a month. He's often out of work."

"What do you mean, 'play the numbers'?"

"Oh, you bet on numbers. You buy tickets with numbers on them, and the winning combinations pay off. Tony's place is one of the places that sells tickets. The cops pulled him in last week for running a gambling place, but he's back in business again."

Kenny was fascinated.

"Have you ever played the numbers?" he asked.

"Who—me?" Joe snorted contemptuously. "After watching my old man lose the grocery money every week? Boy, you can take all that stuff and chuck it as far as I'm concerned—the whole works."

Kenny wasn't quite sure what it was all about, but he didn't ask any more questions. He didn't want Joe to know he didn't really understand.

"There are so many kinds of gambling," Joe said, "and they're all for suckers. I'll stick to peddling papers. If my old man had had brains to keep away from that stuff we'd be able to live in a decent place instead of a lousy dump. Oh well—" he shrugged. "Here we are at Nick's."

They went down two steps into a basement grocery store.

"Hello, Nick," Joe said to the man behind the counter. "The regular order." He plunked down a handful of coins.

Nick hesitated. He glanced suspiciously at Kenny.

"Don't worry about Kenny," said Joe, "he's okay."

Nick ducked into the back room and came back with a brown paper parcel.

"Thanks, Nick. See you in the morning," Joe said as he picked up the bag. "You had Nick worried," he remarked when they were outside. "He's not supposed to sell beer to anyone under age — he'd lose his license. He knows I get it for my old man — that's why he lets me buy it. But he wasn't sure about your being along. He's a good guy. I help him on Saturdays."

The street they had turned into wasn't very well lighted. Greenish shadows flicked over the row of dark, gray houses. A dingy sign reading "Hotel Cadillac" swayed in the wind. Light spilled onto the sidewalks from the basement windows. Through one of them Kenny glimpsed a smoky room crowded with tables. Suddenly the door burst open, and a man stumbled, muttering, on the steps. The blare of a jukebox exploded briefly before the closing door choked off the sound. The man leaned heavily against the building, then sat down abruptly, his head resting in his hands.

Kenny paused. "Should we help him? Is he sick?"

"Come on," said Joe. "He's just drunk." They crossed the street. "Well, here we are," Joe announced, "Home, sweet home!"

Kenny's heart sank. He had been hoping it wouldn't be so bad, but the house was like all the others, gray and sagging, with a rickety porch. A jagged walk led to a dingy side entrance.

As they stepped into a dark hallway a mixture of smells poured over them, a musty basement odor mingled with that of stale fried food and the choking smell of a smoky oil stove. From somewhere Kenny heard the heavy rumble of a man's voice ending abruptly in a curse. He had a sudden impulse to turn and bolt back into the darkness of the street, but he knew it was too late.

"Is that you, Joe?" It was a woman's voice, high-pitched and expressionless. "Have you got Pa's beer?"

At the top of the steps a thin woman with faded-brown hair peered down at them. "Who've you got with you?" she asked.

"This is Kenny, Ma," Joe said, handing her the package. "He's going to wait here for someone to pick him up."

The woman nodded indifferently. "Come in." Then she turned to Joe, "Pa's in the kitchen. Better leave him alone."

Joe led the way into a room lighted from the ceiling by a single, dim bulb. It seemed to be a dining room, living room and bedroom all in one, and was piled with everything imaginable. Kenny tried to keep his face from betraying the sick feeling in the pit of his stomach as he picked his way through the clutter. Baskets bulged with gray, rumpled clothes. An ironing board, piled high with dishes and pans, sagged against the wall. Stumbling over a broken tricycle, Kenny bumped into a rickety carriage where a baby slept.

There was hardly any furniture. In the middle of the room a couple of battered dining-room chairs leaned against a table heaped with toys, comic books and the remains of supper. A brown davenport, the stuffing spilling out of one arm, held a sleeping child. Three other children crouched around a shiny television set in the corner. They were eating potato chips. The oldest, a girl of about ten, turned to eye Kenny solemnly.

"My kid sister, Kathy," Joe said. "The other two are Tommy and Jeff. Well, sit down," he said, pushing one of the chairs toward Kenny. "We might as well watch T.V."

A sudden sound of muffled swearing came from the back room. Kenny glanced at Joe inquiringly.

"Just my old man," Joe remarked. "He took a beating on the horses today — lost twenty-five dollars of his unemployment check. Ma's mad — she was going to pay the rent with it. She and the old man have been jawing at each other all evening."

As if to give proof to his words there was another outburst of sullen mumbling punctuated by the sharp tones of the woman's voice.

"Go on," she shrilled. "Take the other twenty bucks over to Tony's and shoot that too! So the rent won't get paid! So we can't even buy a bag of groceries. What do you care? Never mind if the kids are busting right out of their shoes! You've got your beer, and your races, and your numbers. You're all set!"

The man gave an ugly growl.

"You want to know what you are?" snapped Joe's mother. "You're nothing but a lazy, no-good bum! How do you like that? A lousy bum!"

"Shut up!" There was a sudden scuffle, and the sound of a chair being kicked over.

Without a word Joe was bounding toward the kitchen. Kenny's muscles tightened as he listened, breathless, wondering what he should do. The voices were more muffled now. There was a final explosion of muttered curses, and the man stomped down the back steps. The back door was wrenched open, then slammed shut with an impact that made the house shake. Hurried footsteps pounded sharply along the walk. All was quiet in the kitchen except for Joe's low voice and an occasional muffled sob.

The three children continued to stare at the television screen, munching rhythmically, apparently unconcerned by the disturbance. It was like a weird dream, Kenny thought. He didn't know things like this really happened. Wasn't anyone ever coming for him?

Suddenly Joe reappeared, slicking his hair back with a pocket comb. "Well," he said matter-of-factly, "he's out of the way for a while. Finally took off for Tony's. At least we'll have some peace around here."

He eyed Kenny thoughtfully. "Your old man ever go in for gambling?"

Kenny shook his head. He didn't trust himself to speak. It seemed such a dreadful place and way to live.

MARGARET RITCHIE

Invitation to a Party

Next week Sally would be eleven, and she and her mother were looking through the list of friends she was going to invite to her birthday party.

"Janice, Elaine, Mark, Tina. Who is Tina?" Mother asked. "I don't remember any one by that name in your class."

"Oh, Tina is one of the new kids. A whole batch of them came into our school this month," Sally explained. "Don't you remember? Tina is in my class. She uses some of my books because there aren't enough to go around. I'm helping her with — — "

"She isn't one of the migrant children, is she?" Mother interrupted.

Sally nodded, "Yes, she is. Do you know, Tina has never lived in one place for more than three months in all her life?" Sally exclaimed. "They move from place to place, picking fruit, and vegetables, and stuff wherever there's a harvest. Some of the kids are dumb, but Miss Fergesson said they only seemed that way because they move so much and don't spend much time in school. Tina's mother almost didn't let her come to school, but her father said she had to." Sally stopped for breath.

"Sally," Mother began, "do you think you should invite this Tina to your party?" Then as Sally looked up surprised, she added hastily, "I don't think the migrant workers' children are used to mixing in the community. They have a life of their own in the migrant camp, except for school, of course."

"But Mother, Tina plays with us at school. They all do, except the very scared ones. You should see Tina, Mother! She has the loveliest black hair that curls all over her head." Sally patted her own straight, straw-colored hair. "Tina is one of the prettiest girls in school. Even Joan says so. Besides, I practically told Tina that I was going to invite her to my party."

Sally saw her mother biting her lower lip as she did when she was worried or trying to decide something. "Miss Fergesson says that the whole community needs to be kind to the migrant workers, to help them feel that they belong," she said a little piously.

Mother smiled, "Miss Fergesson is right, but I think you might make sure before you invite Tina whether you are really being kind in asking her to your party."

"I am sure," Sally said, and wrote "Tina" on one of the envelopes and slipped an invitation inside.

"All right," said Mother, "but I have one suggestion — that you all wear the same clothes you wear to school, and make sure that everyone understands that there are to be no party dresses."

"That's a good idea," Sally agreed.

Sally met Tina at the bus next morning.

"I didn't know what address to write so I couldn't send it through the mail," she explained, as she handed Tina a small white envelope.

Tina opened it carefully, and her face brightened as she read the invitation.

"I have to ask my mother," she said shyly, slipping the envelope with its invitation into her pocket.

Every so often during the day Tina felt in her pocket to make sure the invitation was still there. It made her feel happy to know she had it. This was the first school she had been to where the children were friendly. It still surprised her sometimes to be talked to, to be invited to join in games with the others on the playground. She was teased when she did some things, but she didn't mind that at all. Tina hadn't even dreamed of finding a friend like Sally, and now she was invited to a party.

On the way back to the migrant camp Tina sat next to Anna on the bus. While she was wondering whether to tell her about the invitation or not, she heard Anna say, "Think your ma will let you go to the party?"

Tina looked at her in surprise. "How did you know?"

Anna shrugged her shoulders and smiled. "Oh I heard some of the girls in your class talking. They ——" She looked at Tina, "I guess I'd better not tell you any more."

"You might as well."

"Well, all right. I heard one girl say she thought Sally shouldn't have invited you to the party. Another one said she wasn't going if you accepted."

Tina gasped. "I don't believe you, Anna. The girls aren't like that here. You know that. You made the story up because you didn't get asked."

"Honest. I heard them. One girl said it was all right going to school with migrant children, but if her mother knew she was invited to a party with one of them she was sure her mother wouldn't let her go."

"You're lying," Tina said. She turned her back on Anna and felt again the corner of the envelope in her pocket.

The migrant workers and their families lived in one-room cabins that stood close together in long rows on either side of a dirt road. Tina opened the door to hers and smelled the warm odor of cabbage. Her mother was standing by the stove, and Tina looked into the pot to see if there was meat with the cabbage tonight. Small chunks of dark beef came to the surface as her mother stirred. Tina licked her lips.

"It looks good, Ma."

"It should, with meat costing the way it does. What made you so late today?" Her mother stopped stirring and sat down.

"I wasn't any later than usual. It just gets dark sooner." She looked around the cabin. "Where are the kids?"

"Wanda and Jill are out playing. Dan went with Pa to fetch the water."

"Ma, look," Tina laid the envelope on the table. It looked clean and dainty in the dim light of the cabin. Tina hoped the table wasn't too dirty.

"Well, what is it?"

"An invitation. A girl at school is giving a party because she's going to be eleven next Monday." Tina read the invitation out loud.

"Fancy sounding words. How did you get one?"

"Me? I guess she wants me to be there. Can I go?"

Ma put her head back suddenly and laughed. "She wants you to be there! A migrant kid, whose ma and pa break their backs picking beans out in the field all day! That's a good joke." She looked at Tina.

"I guess you can just tell her you won't be there. And if you want reasons," she went on as Tina started to speak, "I'll give you a couple. In the first place, I wouldn't let you. It would only make you unhappy before it was over. In the second place, I couldn't let you. We won't be here then. Don't stand there looking as though I beat you. We have to leave for Florida on Saturday."

"Why are we leaving then?" Tina's voice came out in a whisper at first, and then grew shrill. "We can't move yet. We just got here! The beans aren't all picked yet; we don't need to move. Ma, you're just saying that so I can't go to the party!"

Just then the door opened, and Tina's father and older brother came in. They set the water buckets down by the stove.

"Hi, kid," Tina's father said when he saw her. "Know as much as your pa yet?" He laughed and sat down on the bed in the corner. He unlaced his shoes, emptied the sand onto the floor, and lay back on the bed.

"Pa, listen. Our Tina's had an invitation to a party," Ma said.

"That's nice," Pa murmured.

"It's next Monday," Tina added hopefully. "We won't have to leave here Saturday, will we?" A snore from the bed was her only answer. Tina jumped up from the table and tore the invitation into shreds. Before she could reach the door her mother stopped her and put an arm about her shoulder.

"Listen, Tina," she said. "You don't need their parties or their kindness. You don't get hurt that way, see?" But Tina broke away and faced her mother.

"I guess I don't, and I guess I don't need yours. I don't need anything but filthy, stinking cabins, cabbage soup every night, bumpy rides all over the country in a broken down car ⸺ "

ESTHER BAILEY

How Many Bushels?

"Tony! Tony!" the shrill voice came across the field.

"That's your ma. Hadn't you better get going?" Frank looked a little anxious. Tony put his hands in his pockets and drew a pattern in the sand with his bare toes.

"Not yet," he answered. "She calls like that before the car's half packed. You coming back here next winter?"

"I don't know. I guess so. Gee, I hope you won't stay north."

"Tony!" the voice came again, and then another deeper voice. "Tony!"

"That's Pop. Got to go now." Tony turned and started to run through the field. "See you next year," he called back to Frank over his shoulder.

The brown Plymouth was packed and ready to go. Mattresses

were tied to the roof and covered with a torn piece of canvas. On top of these were an old rocker and a table. Luggage bulged out of the trunk of the car, and the cover was tied down as far as it would go with old pieces of clothesline. Uncle Jed and a friend of his, Mr. Cole, were sitting up front with Pop. The motor was running.

"Hurry, Tony," Ma called from the back seat. Tony squeezed in between her and a large bundle of clothes. As he settled back into the seat he caught sight of his father's face in the rear-view mirror.

"Gee, I had to say good-by to Frank, didn't I?" he explained. "I may never see him again, like Don. I never saw him again and I didn't say good-by. He had my cap pistol too."

The car bumped along the dirt road that took them out to the main highway. The baby in Ma's arms began to whimper. Tony put out a finger and tickled her under the chin. She whimpered more loudly and hid her face in her mother's dress.

"Baby threw up, Ma. Is she sick again?"

Ma nodded.

The old brown car turned onto the highway, and large shiny cars sped past them. Tony's eyes brightened and he whistled as a long, low, cream and red car passed them and disappeared over the next rise.

"Gee," he breathed. "How many bushels would I have to pick to get a car like that?"

Uncle Jed and Mr. Cole laughed loudly. "Let's see," Uncle Jed said. "How many bushels of stuff have you picked, Cole?"

"Oh thousands, maybe billions. Never really learned to count that high. What about you?"

"About the same for me. It'll be years of picking, Tony. You don't see us with shiny new cars, do you?"

"Better start picking as soon as you can, Tony. Ten years is a pretty late start," Uncle Jed teased. Mr. Cole laughed again.

"You stop that talk, Jed," Pop said suddenly. Tony saw Pa's scowl in the mirror. "Tony's going to school. Wherever there's a school for him to go to, he's going. He's not going to end up where you and I are."

"What's wrong with migrants, Pop? I don't need any more school. I can read now. I can read as well as you can, Pop. Mom, you want to know what those signs say?" Tony began to read signs by the side of the road.

"Tony!" his father thundered. "Stop that chatter. You're going to drive us all crazy."

Tony opened his mouth to say something, but changed his mind. He sighed and leaned his head against the bag of clothes in the corner. His eyes felt heavy, and the air that came in the front windows was hot and dry. Soon the voices of the three men in the front seat began to sound like a faraway hum.

Then, without any warning, there was a bang. The car gave a lurch, and it shook and clattered as it went over stones and gravel. It came to a full stop, and leaned against a red sand bank by the side of the road.

"Whew!" Uncle Jed exclaimed. He wiped his face with a kerchief. "That was close."

They slid out of the front seat, and Tony scrambled over fallen bundles to join them. The men were looking at the front left wheel. Bits of tire and tubing were scattered over the road. Tony helped unload the trunk to get the spare tire. As he wheeled it up to the front, Mr. Cole looked at it and shook his head.

"You're not going to get very far on that," he said.

"We've got to," Pa grunted. "Here, someone help me with this tire."

They could hear the baby crying — a weak, sick cry.

"Go and see if Ma wants any help," Pop said without looking up. Tony walked slowly to the other side of the car. His mother was sitting on one of the suitcases, trying to rock the baby to sleep. She handed a half-empty bottle to Tony.

"See if you can get this bottle washed and filled with fresh milk," she said and pointed to a small building about a quarter of a mile up the road.

"Here's a dime, and, Tony," she added, "ask if there is any doctor around here."

"Yes, Ma." Tony turned and walked as fast as he could.

A man was standing behind the counter, and a woman was

sitting in one of the booths when Tony entered the store.

"What do you want?" the man asked. Tony put the bottle on the counter.

"Could you wash this for me, please, and fill it with fresh milk?"

"Got any money?"

Tony showed him the dime, and the man grunted.

"You can't tell. Migrants've been coming in all day. They'd get away without paying if they got a chance — every last one of them. A truckload stopped just before you came. They swarmed all over the place." He emptied the milk out into the sink as he talked and filled the bottle. He didn't wash it very carefully, but Tony didn't dare say anything about that.

"There you are," he said, holding out his hand for the dime. "You a migrant kid?" he asked suddenly.

Tony nodded and started for the door. "You don't know of a doctor near here?" he asked timidly. "There's an awful sick baby in our car."

The man shook his head, but as Tony walked past the booth the woman stopped him.

"Take the next right past this store," she said. "Down the road about ten miles you'll come to a village. Ask for Doctor Jones. Anyone can show you his house. He'll help you."

"Thank you," said Tony and hurried back to the car. His mother was in the car with the baby, and the three men were sitting in the shade looking at a road map. Tony handed the bottle to his mother and squeezed in beside her. The others got into the front seat.

"There's a village about ten miles off the road. A doctor lives there, and a lady in the store thought he might help," Tony reported.

"Well, you think the tire will take the extra miles?" Pop turned to Uncle Jed, who shrugged.

"You saw the tire," he said. "All I know is, if we don't get a picking job in New Jersey we're licked."

Pop looked back at the baby.

"How is she?" he asked Ma.

"Better."

"You decide about the doctor," Pop said. "Do you think we still need one?"

"I can take care of her all right," Ma sighed. "If we did go the extra miles how could we be sure the doctor would look at the baby? Then suppose he'd want to send the baby to a hospital. We can't take time for that," she finished sharply. Pa hesitated.

"Well, what're we waiting for? Let's start," Ma said. Pop turned, started the car, and soon they were off. They passed the store and the turnoff to the village.

"Ma," Tony whispered, "You really think she is better?"

"I said so, didn't I?"

"But you said ――"

"Here," Ma interrupted, changing the subject. "We all had something to eat while you were in the store. Eat this." Tony took the sandwich and bit into it.

Toward dark Uncle Jed took the wheel, and Pop leaned back against the seat and closed his eyes.

"Pop," asked Tony, "we going to travel all night?" His legs felt cramped, and the air in the car was stuffy.

"Hush," his mother said. "Let your Pa sleep. Driving's easier on the tires at night. Besides, the sooner we get there the better. See if you can't sleep."

"I'm not sleepy." Tony tried to amuse himself by guessing what Frank and the other boys would be doing now.

"Ma," he said, "what if the baby dies? Frank's brother died on the trip down south last year. They couldn't find a doctor in time. Can't we go see one?"

"She's sleeping now. She's really better," Ma said. "Here, you hold her a while so I can get some sleep."

Soon Uncle Jed and Tony were the only two awake. Tony tried to stretch his legs without disturbing the baby.

"You awake, Tony?" Uncle Jed said softly.

"Yes. How many more miles have we got to go?" Tony said.

"Oh, more than a thousand, I guess. Been over this road so many times I never stop to figure."

"Uncle Jed, do you ever wish you were anything besides a

migrant worker?" Tony asked softly.

"I don't know. I suppose when I was your age I wished I was doing something else. Got used to this life, though, and I don't know how to do anything else. Why do you ask?"

"I was just wondering," Tony hesitated. "Just wondering what it would be like not to be a migrant kid. Maybe to live in one place for a while."

ESTHER BAILEY

Terrible Secrets!

The girls had stopped to rest after a game of tag on the school playground.

"Look!" said Ann, pointing to the gate. "That must be the new girl the teacher said was coming today."

"Oh, yes," said Donna knowingly, "That's Jane Atkins."

"Do you think we should go over and ask her to play with us?" asked Mary.

"Let's," answered Sally. "I remember how I felt when we moved and I first came to this school. Nobody said a word to me except the teacher."

"I don't think I'm going to like her," said Donna. "She looks kind of funny to me."

"Maybe we should wait until we know her better," said Anna. "Then we won't have to bother to get rid of her if we don't like her."

"I didn't mean that, exactly," said Donna. "Don't you think she looks funny — kind of nervous, maybe?"

"What do you mean?" said Mary. "I think she looks nice."

"Well, I mean jittery — like something is wrong."

"I felt jittery and nervous like something was wrong," said Sally, "the first day I came."

"I don't mean jittery like that," Donna was persistent. She went on in a low voice, "I mean jittery over trying to keep some terrible secret and afraid people are going to find out about it!"

"Do you think she has a terrible secret?" whispered Mary.

"I know she does," said Donna. "Listen, and I'll tell you!" The four girls drew closer together. "Her father is in jail! He stole some money from the bank where he worked in Chicago."

"How do you know that?" asked Ann, gasping with astonishment.

"My mother knows her family, that's how," said Donna. "My mother is sorry they moved here. They'll run down the neighborhood."

"I feel sorry for her," said Sally.

"But we can't have friends like that," said Mary.

"Mary is right," Donna insisted. "We'll just ignore her. Maybe she, and her mother, and little brother will move somewhere else if people treat them the way they deserve to be treated."

"She can't help it because her father stole money from the bank," said Sally thoughtfully.

"Well, no," admitted Donna. "I guess she couldn't keep her father from taking the money. But how do we know she isn't a thief too?"

"We don't," said Sally, "but we can't accuse her of stealing until we catch her at it."

"I bet we will," said Donna. "I'm going to watch out for her."

"Do you think when you grow up and get married you will get a divorce just because your mother did?" asked Sally.

"That's different," said Donna angrily.

Mary was beginning to wonder. "Catholics think getting a divorce is a sin," she said. "I'm a Catholic, and I have to think what your mother did is a sin."

"I'll bet every family in the world has something they don't want everyone to know about," said Sally.

"Not in *my* family," Donna declared.

"What do you mean, Sally?" asked Ann.

"Oh, you know — like a family skeleton in the closet," answered Sally. "That's what my father calls it — our problem, I mean."

"Did he steal something too?" asked Donna.

"No, he didn't," said Sally. "But he did something that some people might think was just as bad. He used to be an alcoholic."

"What's that?" asked Ann.

"Somebody who gets drunk," answered Sally. "He used to get drunk, and come home, and just act terrible. He would make my mother cry and he scared me and my sister."

"What happened?" asked Mary.

"He joined a sort of club called Alcoholics Anonymous. They are all people who used to drink too much. They help people who want to stop. Daddy had to work hard to get over his problem. He says he never could have done it if people had not been kind to him and helped him."

"Well, that's different," said Donna. "It's not as bad as stealing."

"Some of our neighbors thought it was terrible," said Sally. "They acted as if it were worse than stealing. They wouldn't speak to us and they wouldn't let us play with their children."

"Let's play tag some more." Donna wanted to change the subject. She didn't like the way the conversation was going.

"I'm going over and say hello to Jane," said Sally.

Mary hesitated. She was thinking about the time her father had been fired from his job, and how her mother kept saying over and over again that it was disgraceful. She remembered how her mother had told her she must never tell *anyone* that Daddy had been fired.

Ann hesitated too. Her mother had made her promise *never* to tell anyone that her grandparents couldn't read and write. She remembered how scared she had always been that someone would find out about it.

Donna tossed her head and walked in the other direction. She felt sure that no one in her family had ever done anything that could be questioned, and she was sure they never would.

MARJORIE LEAMING

For the Teacher

The hope is that these stories will encourage spontaneous discussion among the children. However, in instances where the children are slow to involve themselves in discussion the teacher may want to take some of the questions and ideas in the following pages and rephrase them according to the needs of the particular children in her group. These are not intended as a list of questions that *should* be asked; rather, they are points of departure which the teacher may use for starting discussion.

An effort has been made in all of the questions to phrase them so that the involvement of the child will be with the child or children of the story. It is very important to keep the children's discussion on a non-personal level so that the class will not pass over into therapy, and equally important that the child shall not be asked to pass judgment on the behavior of the parents or teachers in the stories. The primary purpose of the stories in this book is to help children to think in terms of their social relations with other children, and this purpose will be best served if the discussion is kept as objective as possible.

Ideas and Questions for Discussion

HARRIET'S PRESENTS
(Page 3)

If you were Harriet how would you feel about the dress? About the handkerchiefs? Act out what Harriet might have said if she had pleaded with her mother to let her do as the rest did.

Suppose you were Adele. What could you have said or done instead of joining in the game of making fun of Harriet? Would this have helped?

Could the girls do anything for Harriet? Would it help if Harriet were able to talk about the situation? What would have happened if Adele had been able to buy an extra present for Harriet to give? Does Harriet know that she is different?

Act out Harriet's response if Adele did buy a present for her to give. What would she do with the handkerchiefs?

Have you known similar situations? What did you do?

THE OUTSIDER
(Page 5)

Would Arthur have been better off if his mother had let him stay inside with his books?

Does Arthur secretly wish to be like the other boys?

Should the boys accept him outside of class since they admire him for what he can do in class?

Is it possible for a person to change the way he is? Does Arthur have a chance of becoming like the other boys?

Will Arthur feel differently when he is grown up? Or is the fact that he is left out and ignored a sign that this will continue?

Act out what might happen if Arthur asked the boys to teach him about the things that interest them.

Play out the rest of the story. What do you think *did* happen when Arthur joined the boys?

REPLACEMENT FOR BILL
(Page 8)

Can people with different interests still be friends?

Should we have one best friend who does everything we like to do, or would it be better if we had many friends and did different things with each of them?

If Jim tried, could he learn to like music and enjoy it with Stephen? Could Stephen learn to like Jim's games? Is this important?

Can a new friend replace an old one?

Is it necessary to be friends with the boy next door?

What is it like to be a new boy in town? Is it more difficult for a boy like Stephen, who has interests which are different from the others?

What are some other things families do together the way Stephen's family play and enjoy music? Is one activity better than another?

How are "special friends" chosen? What things count?

NATURE STUDY
(Page 12)

Why are the boys making fun of Peter? Do they really dislike nature study?

What might be some of the reasons Peter has for bringing these things to school?

Can one have special interests, share them with his schoolmates, and still not irritate them?

Did the boys take the things to school on Monday? If so, which of these responses might Miss Smith have made? Did she go along with the joke and laugh with the boys? Did she take them seriously? Did she become angry? What other responses might she have made?

Act out what might have happened when the boys brought in the stick, leaves, and stone.

How would Peter have acted if the boys had gone through with their plan?

NO ROOM FOR JERRY
(Page 14)

Is it fair to have a parent, teacher, or playground director insist that someone who plays so badly that he spoils the game be included?

What could the boys do to help Jerry? Should they try to, or is it his own fault for not trying to help himself?

Is it dishonest for the children to play where they know their mothers can't see them?

What might Jerry have been thinking when the boys were threatening him at the end of the story?

Did Jerry really want to be a part of the group?

THREE STRIKES AND OUT
(Page 16)

Why did striking out make Ronnie so angry?

Are there other ways of refusing to accept failure? Is it the same thing when one makes excuses, quits, claims the equipment was at fault, or says this is not a "good day"?

Why do children fight? Is it always for the same reason?

What might the children have done about Ronnie that could have helped him?

Does Ronnie's superiority as a player give him the right to act this way?

Do major-league ball players ever behave in this manner? What is the penalty?

MAMA'S BOY
(Page 18)

Did Fatty really think the boys would hurt him? What has made him the way he is?

What made the boys think they had had fun? Would they have felt sorry if Fatty had been hurt?

Would any of the boys have done this if he had been alone? Did being in a group make it seem funny?

Why did the boys tease Fatty? What did it do to Fatty to be picked on? What effect did it have on the boys?

Suppose one member of the group had been sympathetic to Fatty? Could he have done anything? Act out what might have happened if he had tried.

Under what circumstances can jokes become serious matters?

TICKET TO A FOOTBALL GAME
(Page 23)

Act out the conversation between Paul and his father. What might Paul have said? Should he have been punished and, if so, how?

Is sneaking into a game the same thing as stealing?

Suppose Paul had taken his mother's money and used it instead. Would this have been different? Try acting out how he would have told his mother about it and what she would have said and done.

Should children be given advances on their allowance? If so, under what circumstances?

What other things might Paul have done which would have been as dishonest as sneaking into the game?

THE DREAM CAMP
(Page 27)

Would the girls have thought less of Nancy if they had known she was not going to camp?

Act out a possible scene in which Nancy admits to the girls that she made up the camp she told them about.

Did Nancy really mean to lie, or was she carried away by her own story after she started to tell it? Does this make a difference?

How is it possible to distinguish between a tall tale and dishonesty?

Note: A book about a similar situation, humorously portrayed, is: *And To Think That I Saw It On Mulberry Street* by Dr. Seuss. New York: The Vanguard Press, 1937.

WHY JANIE CHEATED
(Page 29)

What are some of the reasons other children in the class might have had for cheating?

Was Janie more unhappy about the cheating or about going home with poor marks?

What about the girl who gave Janie the answers? Was she cheating too?

How can the girls help Janie? What can Janie do about the situation? Act out several possible scenes where the girls and Janie are talking, where Janie is talking to her mother or the teacher, or where Janie is talking with her older sister.

If a teacher is not aware of the cheating in a class, does this excuse the children?

MAKING THE TEST EASIER
(Page 31)

How does the cheating in this story differ from Janie's?

What about the child who has learned the answers and wants to be honest? Or the child who knows the material and doesn't care if he is honest, but wants to be the best in the class?

Act out what might have happened if the boys had gone ahead with their plan. Act out the discussion they might have had if they decided not to do it.

How might the boys' parents have felt if they had known about the plan?

Did the fact that the boys learned part of the lesson make it less serious to cheat on the rest of it?

WHAT DIFFERENCE DOES IT MAKE?
(Page 33)

Is there a conflict for Nancy between cheating and being loyal to Marie?

How do you think Nancy and Marie will feel about each other the next day? Will it affect their friendship permanently?

If it is true that "almost everyone cheats" in a classroom, does it make a difference?

Act out what Marie might have said or done if the teacher had seen her cheating.

YOU TOOK IT
(Page 34)

Was Joy blamed only because she was the last in the washroom?

Are there children in our schools or our neighborhoods that we know we can blame?

What could Agnes have said to Joy at the end of the story? Act this out.

Did these children have the habit of blaming Joy for everything?

Joy *was* the last one in the washroom. Did this give the children the right to be suspicious?

Note: An instructive experiment is to show the class a picture of an accident, or something with much detail. Have the children study it, and then remove it. Ask questions about it. Are our memories accurate?

THE BLUE SOLDIER
(Page 37)

How would Jay have felt if he had managed to return the soldier to the counter? Would he still have stolen?

Would it have been different if Jay had been a child who had almost no toys at home?

Was putting the soldier in the ash can a real solution? What did he accomplish by getting rid of the soldier?

Would it have been worse if Jay had stolen something that cost fifty cents or a dollar instead of a soldier that cost only a nickel or a dime?

Do small children sometimes do things like this? Is this considered stealing? How do they learn not to steal?

PRICE OF ADMISSION
(Page 39)

What might happen at the next club meeting?

Will Pete break down and tell his mother because he feels so unhappy?

What might happen if Pete does tell his mother and she tells the other mothers?

Is this behavior the same as that shown by children who throw stones at windows in an empty building?

Act out what might have happened in the club if Pete had refused to steal?

Suppose one of the boys had been caught while he was paying the price of admission. Act out what the other boys could have said and done.

Suppose the boy who got caught was put under pressure to tell who else was involved. What would he have done?

THE UNHAPPY PARTY
(Page 45)

Were the children really sorry, or were they just saying so?

Do you think the children should be made to buy new curtains? What else could they do?

Could anyone except an adult have stopped them after they had started?

Whose fault was it? The one who started it? The ones who joined? The ones who laughed and thought it was funny? The ones who disapproved and said nothing?

Did all the children feel the same about the behavior at the party?

WHICH TO DO?
(Page 47)

Do adults also sometimes want to do two or more things at the same time? How do you think they solve the problem? Is it too hard a question for a child to decide?

What do you think Diane decided? What values were involved in each of the things she wanted to do?

If it had been two parties, or two trips, instead of a trip versus an activity involving many others, would this have made a difference?

Is it fair to make an absolute rule like this one about the last rehearsal? Why are such rules made?

Did Diane really want her parents to make the decision for her? What happens to children if this is done?

Would the decision that Diane's father and mother made have been the same one she would probably make? What makes you think so?

How would you decide which of two or more things you wanted to do was the most important?

OLD CLOTHES
(Page 51)

When you give old clothes away should they be cleaned and mended, or should the people who receive them take care of this?

Is there as much meaning in giving something you don't care about as there is in giving up something in order that you may share with someone?

Why do you think Debbie didn't want to try on the new clothes?

How did Mildred want Debbie to feel and act? Why was gratitude so important to her?

How do children feel about wearing their older brothers' and sisters' clothes? Is this different from Debbie's feeling?

Why did the people by the tracks beg for more gifts when Debbie could not accept them?

Do people who are poor and live as Debbie did mind it?

What organizations are there that clean and mend old clothes and then sell them to the poor at prices they can afford to pay? Is this a better way to give?

Note: The teacher may suggest a discussion of Maimonides' "Eight Degrees of Charity." (Maimonides was a great Hebrew theologian, rabbi, and medical doctor. He was born in 1135 and died in 1204. His Eight Degrees of Charity have survived through the years.) We quote them in full, although the teacher will want to simplify them in presenting them to younger children.

There are eight degrees or steps in the duty of charity.

The first and lowest degree is to give, but with reluctance or regret. This is the gift of the hand, but not of the heart.

The second is, to give cheerfully, but not proportionately to the distress of the suffered.

The third is, to give cheerfully, and proportionately, but not until solicited.

The fourth is, to give cheerfully, proportionately, and even unsolicited, but to put it in the poor man's hand, thereby exciting in him the painful emotion of shame.

The fifth is, to give charity in such a way that the distressed may receive the bounty, and know their benefactor, without their being known to him. Such was the conduct of some of our ancestors, who used to tie up money in the corners of their cloaks, so that the poor might take it unperceived.

The sixth, which rises still higher, is to know the objects of our bounty but remain unknown to them. Such was the conduct of those of our ancestors who used to convey their charitable gifts into poor people's dwellings, taking care that their own persons and names should remain unknown.

The seventh is still more meritorious, namely, to bestow charity in such a way that the benefactor may not know the relieved persons, nor they the names of their benefactors, as was done by our charitable forefathers during the existence of the temple. For there was in that holy building a place called the Chamber of the Silent, wherein the good deposited secretly whatever their generous hearts suggested, and from which the poor were maintained with equal secrecy.

Lastly, the eighth, and the most meritorious of all, is to anticipate charity by preventing poverty; namely, to assist the reduced fellowman, either by a considerable gift, or a sum of money, or by teaching him a trade, or by putting him in the way of business, so that he may earn an honest livelihood, and not be forced to the dreadful alternative of holding out his hand for charity. This is the highest step and the summit of charity's golden ladder.

WE LIKE TO HELP
(Page 53)

Do people have different feelings because they are poor?

Have these children who brought things from home really shared?

Is the point of the United Nations' "Trick or Treat" collection spoiled if an elaborate party is given for the children after the collection has been made?

Is it good for children to feel superior as the children in the story do, for instance when Sally says, "It makes me feel so good."

Is helping at home, which has little glamor, as important as giving to charity?

Are Thanksgiving baskets really a good idea?

How do we know what are our real reasons for giving?

IT'S MY SLED!
(Page 56)

If Fred went to the country alone would he enjoy sliding down the hill as many times as he wanted to?

Make a poster of safety rules that children need for coasting.

Can children be as selfish in demanding that another child share as the other child is in not wanting to share?

Should we be as careful of other people's things as we are of our own? Are we?

Should children be expected to share toys while they are still new?

RENA'S REPORT CARD
(Page 58)

What might be the reasons why Rena's report card was so poor? Does it make a difference if she tried and still had poor marks?

Did making fun of the teacher solve anything for Rena?

What might Rena have done when she got home with her report card?

Do rewards at home make children study harder?

What would have helped Rena to accept her card, since she already knew what she would probably find on it?

Will she do better next time? Under what circumstances?

HER MAJESTY THE QUEEN
(Page 60)

What about Patty's complaint that she didn't even have a chance to try out for the part of the queen? Is it fair to leave out a child because he or she doesn't look the part?

Was Carol cheating when she read the part ahead of time?

Are the prompters, those who make the costumes, those who plan the scenery, as important as those who have the leading parts in a play? Is this as satisfying? Why?

Should all the children have turns taking important parts, or is it better to have the best ones do them every time? Does the child who can not read well sometimes have the greater need to be chosen?

What made Carol so selfish? Is it her fault? What can be done to help her? Does she want to change?

WAR GAMES
(Page 68)

Are children more likely to fight while playing "war games" than at other times?

Does telling Dan not to play war games help make the world more peaceful?

Do you think Dan's father would also say he can not watch battles on television? Is this the same as playing games?

Where did Rob and Dan get the ideas that they were fighting about?

Had these children really thought about war?

Act out what happens after the children walk off and leave Rob and Dan alone.

Act out what Dan might have said to his father when he got back home and what his father might have answered.

HOW LONG A JUMP?
(Page 73)

Was it fair to change the rules for Fred because he was blind? Would it have been better to make up some new tests for him?

Blindfold yourselves and act out how it feels not to be able to see. What difference does the fact that you know you can take off the blindfold make? What are the hard things to do when you can not see? What things are easier?

Try recognizing various objects just by feeling them. Are some easier to recognize than others? What things can you not find out about by just feeling?

Notes: The teacher might tell the story of Helen Keller and how much she was able to do in spite of being blind and deaf.

Some books about blind children, Seeing Eye dogs, and the use of Braille are:

Chevigny, Hector. *My Eyes Have a Cold Nose.* New Haven: Yale University Press.

Hartwell, Dickson. *Dogs Against Darkness.* New York: Dodd, Mead & Co.

Johnson, Margaret S. and Johnson, Helen L. *Vicki, A Guide Dog.* New York: Harcourt, Brace & Co.

Vance, Marguerite. *Windows for Rosemary.* New York: E. P. Dutton & Co., Inc.

SALLY'S HOMEWORK
(Page 77)

Why did Mrs. Downer jump to the conclusion that the girls

were teasing Sally? What are some similar instances in which we misinterpret the behavior of others?

How can we show handicapped people that we accept them for themselves and avoid making them feel that our friendship is really pity?

How do we really feel in the presence of handicapped people? Do we enjoy them? Do we feel embarrassed? Do we feel sorry for them? How does this affect your relationship with them? How does this make them feel?

Try to imagine what it would be like to have never heard a single sound. How does this make it hard to learn to talk, to read, to dance, to do all the things that others do?

Notes: For younger children the book, *Tim and His Hearing Aid* by Eleanor Ronnei (New York: Dodd, Mead & Co.) might be helpful. Discuss the problem of the hard of hearing as opposed to the totally deaf.

For older children the *National Geographic* for March, 1955 has an excellent article on the Clarke School and the teaching of the deaf: Grosvenor, Lillian and Culver, Willard. "Deaf Children Learn to Talk at Clarke School." Volume CVII, No. 3, pp. 379-398.

HIS FACE LOOKS FUNNY
(Page 80)

Are there classes for retarded children in your school? How do you feel about these children? How do you talk about them?

How does the fact that they will never grow up mentally make them really differ from children whose age they act?

What games could Kathy and the little boy play that both would enjoy?

Does the retarded child need to play with other children? What things might he learn by doing this? What might we learn by playing with him?

How can Kathy be helped to see that an apparently small gain is really a great step in learning for the little boy?

We say that there is no disgrace in being dull. Is there any cause for pride in being bright?

IT'S HARD TO REMEMBER
(Page 82)

What could the children have done when Al finally got back into the classroom? Act out his entrance and what the children did and said.

How does one know when to offer help to a handicapped person? How do they feel about help?

Whose fault was it that Al was forgotten? How could it have been avoided?

How can we live up to our decisions after they have been made? The children in this story were thoughtless. Is this likely to happen again?

THE LOST BALL
(Page 85)

How might the children solve the problem if a ball goes into Mrs. Warren's yard again?

Why are the children afraid of Mrs. Warren? Could they be friends with her? Did she really believe they were spies?

Do you think the children will really leave Mrs. Warren alone?

Why did Tommy eat up all the club candy while he was feeling sorry for himself? Should he tell the boys about it or just replace the candy?

Why did Tommy feel better after he had talked to his father and the policeman? Does just talking about something help us?

Note: If the children seem to want to discuss mental illness rather than their attitude toward people like Mrs. Warren, it would probably be best to ask a psychologist, a psychiatrist, or a social worker to come in and help with the class discussion.

WE NEED OUR FRIENDS
(Page 95)

How would you have felt if you had been one of John's friends who came to call? Would you have wanted to go? Do you think they should have come? What would you have said?

Should John have stayed home instead of going to his friend's house for supper?

Why did it help John to tell all the things his father had done and said that morning? Did it help to have the boys listen?

Would it have been better if the boys had sent flowers instead of coming to visit?

Notes: The teacher might have the class act out the boys' visit with the teacher playing the role of the bereaved child.

The teacher will want to have these pamphlets available to help with her thinking:

Klaber, Florence. *When Children Ask About Death.* Society for Ethical Culture, 2 West 64th Street, New York 23, N. Y.

Wolf, Anna W. M. *Helping Your Child to Understand Death.* Child Study Association of America, Inc., 132 East 74th Street, New York 21, N. Y.

WILL YOU PLAY?
(Page 97)

Why did the girls think that Rachel should not play? How would you have felt if you had been one of the girls?

Did the girls think there was something mysterious about death? Why were they so interested in the body, the funeral home, the funeral, and what would happen to the children?

What should people do when someone dies?

Did the fact that Rachel wanted to play mean that she did not love her mother?

Do the girls really disapprove of Rachel's playing, or are they afraid to play with her?

FIRST WEEK END OF THE MONTH
(Page 99)

If parents argue, does this mean that they do not like each other?

Is it good for Roberta to be able to get things by going to her father for them? Why do you think so?

Would Roberta want the girls to postpone the cookout until some other week end? Should they?

Do you think the week ends with father are as gay as Roberta claims? Why does she want the girls to think so?

SHALL WE INVITE THE FATHERS?
(Page 101)

Is Ruth being selfish when she asks to have the play in the afternoon? Why does she feel different from the children whose fathers might not come because they work nights?

When do you think the program should be held?

What can the class do to make Ruth comfortable if the program is held in the evening? Do you think Ruth should stay home if she feels as she does?

Can Ruth still love both of her parents? Can she be a happy child?

Suppose Ruth had disliked her father. Must she pretend to love him because he is her father?

I DON'T UNDERSTAND
(Page 103)

Should Mary have written to her aunt without telling her mother? Could Aunt Ruth change things?

Why did the divorce seem worse to Mary when she heard the other children talking about it?

Would it have helped Mary if she had told Mrs. West about what was troubling her? Would this have helped as much as talking to her mother?

How did talking with her mother help Mary? Would this make it easier to face the children the next day?

In what ways will life be difficult for Mary now? Will it always affect her relations with the other children? Can she learn to live as happily the new way?

WHAT WILL THE OTHERS THINK?
(Page 107)

Why was Joyce so concerned about what the other children would think? What might they have been thinking and saying?

How can Joyce help her father to feel more comfortable when he comes home again? Will it be hard for Joyce? For her father?

Do you think talking to the nurse would help Joyce?

Act out the point at which Joyce gets the courage to discuss her problem with the children and tell them where her father is. What would the children and Joyce say?

Act out the discussion the teacher might have had with the class while Joyce was still in the nurse's office. What might the children say when they have had a chance to talk about it?

LET'S BE FRIENDS ANYWAY
(Page 113)

Are you able to tell your friends what you believe rather than just saying that you do not believe what they do? What would you tell them?

How important is the right to question everything? Are liberals the only ones who do this?

How can we find out what Catholics really believe? Is it important for us to know?

Do we have to believe the same things about religion as our friends do in order to play with them? Is it desirable to discuss religion with them?

Should a church have a short statement of belief which can be quoted?

Are the children in the story really arguing about the important things in their religions?

Was Chuck really baiting his Catholic friends, or were they tormenting him?

Are Chuck and Jimmy showing a form of smugness about their religion which might be the real cause of the trouble?

STRANGE CHURCHES
(Page 117)

If Jim's church does not permit him to visit other churches, did he do wrong to go to the worship service, even though it was so short? Why was Jim so upset?

Why does the Catholic church seem so mysterious and strange to Bruce? Does Bruce's church seem as strange to Jim?

Would practice in explaining our religion to others help us to avoid having to say, "You just wouldn't understand my church"?

Note: If children want to discuss the Catholic church, two good books are:

Fitch, Florence Mary. *One God, The Ways We Worship Him.* New York: Lothrop, Lee and Shepard Co.

Manwell, Reginald and Fahs, Sophia L. *The Church Across the Street.* Boston: The Beacon Press.

THE BUTTERFLY COLLECTION
(Page 123)

If Negro children will not be admitted in a place where a mixed group is going, what should the group do? Should Dave's mother have insisted Pete be invited to go swimming?

Act out what might have happened at the farm if Mother had accepted the invitation for Dave and Pete without explaining that Pete was a Negro.

Are there equal values in having a fine collection that is recognized as good and in getting a prize? What are the things that can happen when prizes are offered?

Try to imagine Pete's feelings when he goes back to the south after having had relatively pleasant experiences in the north.

Why did the people in the neighborhood where Pete's family were living sign the petition? Do they have a right to say who they want for neighbors?

Pete tells about the places where his family could not eat or stay. Does this happen in your city? What can we do when it happens?

Pretend you belong to a Negro family who have just found out that the neighbors do not want them living nearby. Play out the conversation.

Notes: A good book for the children would be: Benedict, Ruth and Weltfish, Gene. *In Henry's Backyard.* New York: Henry Schuman.

For the teacher, a good book is: Clark, Kenneth B. *Prejudice and Your Child.* Boston: The Beacon Press.

THE OTHERS LEAVE EARLY
(Page 133)

Does sending Protestant, Catholic, and Jewish children from the public schools to their own churches emphasize religious differences and cause more friction among the children?

Why does Cindy feel uncomfortable about not going to the weekday classes?

What do you think Cindy told the other children about her church?

Is weekday religious education desirable? Would you like to have it?

Why did Cindy's parents not allow her to go with one of the other groups of children since she could not go to her own church?

I VOTE WE KEEP MARYANN!
(Page 135)

Does it make a difference because Maryann does not believe that saluting the flag is wrong? What would you do?

Must we believe as our parents do?

Would you vote to keep Maryann?

Should the children let the teacher decide this issue? Would different teachers make different decisions?

What other things, which children find difficult to understand, do parents sometimes ask children to believe?

Should Maryann just have stayed home rather than try to work out the problem?

THE MYSTERIOUS NEIGHBORS
(Page 138)

Where did Mary Jane get her ideas? Was she really convinced at the end of the story?

Are we sometimes unfair when it comes to appraising orthodox Protestant churches? Are they harder for us to understand than the Catholic and Jewish faiths?

What made Rachel's family seem mysterious? The things they believed, or the strange foods they ate and the different holidays they celebrated?

In what ways are Hanukkah and Christmas alike?

WHY CAN'T LIFE STAY SIMPLE?
(Page 146)

What did Dick do after the story ended? How did he feel about it?

Would the boys come to hold a different point of view after the Jewish boy has lived near them longer? Is this temporary, or are they likely to continue to feel this way?

Do we have to play with everyone who lives in our neighborhood?

How should we choose our friends?

How can we learn to enjoy people whose background is different from our own? To what extent should our feelings about other people be the same as our parents' feelings?

Is there a difference between the verbal agreement not to sell in this story and the signing of a petition? Do we have the right to decide who our neighbors will be?

How are stereotypes about other groups developed, and how do we learn them?

Two pamphlets that will help the teacher in this last discussion are:

Allport, G. W. and Kramer, B. M. *Some Roots of Prejudice.* CCI Reports, No. 1. Commission on Community Interrelations of the American Jewish Congress, 212 West 50th Street, New York 19, N. Y.

Van Til, William. *Prejudiced—How Do People Get That Way?* Anti-Defamation League of B'nai B'rith, 515 Madison Avenue, New York 22, N. Y.

Note: If children are not familiar with Jewish customs some good books are:

Fitch, Florence Mary. *One God, The Ways We Worship Him.* New York: Lothrop, Lee and Shepard Co.

Manwell, Reginald and Fahs, Sophia L. *The Church Across the Street.* Boston: The Beacon Press.

Gilbert, Arthur and Tarcov, Oscar. *Your Neighbor Celebrates.* New York: Friendly House Publishers.

Goldberg, Rabbi David. *Holidays for American Judaism.* New York: Bookman Associates.

MEXICAN OR BALL PLAYER?
(Page 148)

Why did Jim dislike Ramon?

Do we sometimes dislike people because they are more skillful than we?

In your community which groups have become scapegoats? Japanese? Italians? Irish? French? Negroes? Polish? Mexicans? Swedes? Why does this vary from one section of the country to another?

Have you known Negroes or Mexicans whose parents had the same education as your own? Would this make a difference?

Do you know any schools in the north that are all Negro? Why might this be so?

What can we do about problems of this kind?

MOVING DAY—SOPHIATOWN
(Page 153)

Why weren't the children allowed to talk about the situation? Why were the parents so angry when the children said anything about hating white people?

Why did both children and parents have to pretend that what was happening didn't matter?

Is there more hope for us than there is for South Africa? What are the differences?

What can the Negro in South Africa or here do to help the situation? What can we do?

Do you think that there are real differences between Negroes and Whites?

Do these problems exist in your community?

TWO DINKY ROOMS
(Page 160)

Have you ever belonged to a group that was as different as the Fellowship described in this story? How did you feel?

Why did the Martins drive twenty miles to a church? Do you agree with John that this was stupid?

Could they have been happy in a neighborhood church if they had tried?

Does one need a special building and a large group of people to have a church?

What does the building contribute to the activities of a church?

How are the things that you are studying different from those that your friends study?

Does the only Catholic or Jew in a Protestant neighborhood feel as strange as the only Protestant in a Catholic or Jewish neighborhood?

SHE DOESN'T SPEAK A WORD OF ENGLISH!
(Page 167)

Why was it so exciting to have Rosa in the room at first? Why did the excitement wear off?

Was it stupid of Rosa to forget so many words? Did she really try to remember?

Why is English so difficult to learn? Think for instance of such things as: *ough* as it is pronounced in *cough, through, thought, though;* or *blew* and *blue* which are spelled differently but pronounced the same; or a word like *bow*, which is spelled the same but has different meanings, as "I will *bow* after I say my piece," or "I have a new *bow* and arrow." What other examples can you think of? What happens to a child like Rosa when she meets these words?

What effect did the comments about Rosa repeated from home have on the children's attitudes?

What may happen when Rosa does come back?

THAT POLISH COSTUME
(Page 170)

As Helenka grows older are she and her mother likely to quarrel more or less? About what things?

Act out what happens the day of the party between Helenka and her mother. What will Helenka do? Will she wear the costume? Will she be sick? Will she get another costume and change before she goes to school? Will she wear what her mother wants her to?

Act out what might happen at the party if Helenka wears the Polish costume.

What can we do for these second-generation children to make them feel more comfortable?

Are there times when things seem very important to us and at the same time appear trivial to our parents? What occasions can you remember?

Do the older and younger generation tend to disagree even when they do not have a foreign background? About what things?

HIS BROTHER IS A COWARD
(Page 174)

What did Joe do after the story ended?

How often do we accept labels? Such as thinking that anyone who won't fight is a coward, or a Communist, etc.? Can you think of specific examples?

Does a pacifist refuse to fight out of faith or fear? Why do you think so?

What are some of the ways in which men have tried to establish peace? Is this an ideal that can never be achieved? Is it important to us?

Do people have a right to hold opinions which are so contrary to those of the majority?

Do you think the United Nations may make some progress toward world peace?

WHAT WILL HAPPEN TO US?
(Page 177)

Do people sometimes get mean and spiteful, or give up trying, when they have been poor for a long time? How can we understand the feelings of a family which has been on relief, never had things other people have, etc.?

How many social problems can you find in this story? How do you feel about unemployment, the responsibility of industry for an injured man, the hiring of the physically handicapped, etc.?

What would it be like to live as these people do, never being sure how much longer you will have a job? What happens to the family when the father is unemployed?

Does any group in your city work on the problem of hiring the handicapped? If interested in this phase of the problem you could ask some representative of this group to discuss it with you.

THE STRIKE
(Page 181)

How does the strike affect the children? Do you side with Sally, who thinks it is unfair, or with David, who feels it is so important?

Why do unions strike? What other things do you think workers might do? Do you need more facts? If so a book that will help is: Shippen, Katherine B. *This Union Cause.* New York: Harper and Brothers.

Note: The teacher might be interested in reading, and sharing in part with the children, John Greenway's *American Folk Songs of Protest.* (Philadelphia: University of Pennsylvania Press.) A number of the songs in this book have been issued on a record, *American Industrial Folksongs,* Riverside Folk Lore Series 12-607. Many children already know "Sixteen Tons" which is included both in the book and on the record.

NIGHT IN TOWN
(Page 186)

How will Joe turn out? Will the way his father is make him work twice as hard? Or will he too give up before he is a grown man?

Do you think a family living in such poverty should have a television set? If not, who is to blame? The father who is weak? The children who perhaps teased for one? The store that made it so easy to buy on time?

Do people really live like the family in this story? How do you think they feel about it? Why should they concern us?

Is there anything Kenny can do for Joe and his family? If so, what?

INVITATION TO A PARTY
(Page 192)

Act out what might have happened after Tina's outburst to her mother.

Act out Sally's reaction when she finds that Tina has left and isn't coming to the party.

Act out what might have happened if Tina had come to the party. Would the girls have stayed away?

Why wouldn't Tina's mother let her go to the party? What did she mean when she said she didn't want Tina to be hurt?

How much education do these children get going from school to school and never staying in one school long enough to finish a grade? Is this important?

Note: A good book for the teacher to read is: Greene, Shirley. *The Education of Migrant Children.* Department of Rural Education, National Education Association, 1201 Sixteenth Street, N.W., Washington, D. C.

HOW MANY BUSHELS?
(Page 196)

Why did the family not take the baby to the doctor? Was it because they didn't have money? Because they thought he wouldn't see them? Because they were afraid he would send the baby to a hospital? Because the tires were so poor? Because they didn't care?

Does Tony have a chance to rise above the situation and become something other than a migrant worker?

Imagine the feelings of a child like Tony who sees other children with so many things he has never had. How do you think this might affect Tony?

Do you think these people really like living this way?

TERRIBLE SECRETS!
(Page 201)

Should children be blamed for what their parents have done?

Should Donna have kept her knowledge to herself? Why was she so eager to share it with the other children? Why was Sally the most sympathetic?

Do you think the class accepted Jane after all, or did they refuse to play with her?

What is likely to happen if something gets stolen in the school during the next few weeks?

How can we recognize gossip when we hear it? How can we overcome the temptation to repeat it?

Notes on the Authors

Esther Bailey was born in Portuguese East Africa, where her parents are still missionaries. She attended school through high school in Pietermaritztrug, South Africa. She came to America in 1946 and attended Vesper George School of Art, specializing in illustration with particular interest in children's book illustration. She now lives in Hollis, New York, where her husband, Rev. Ralph C. Bailey, is the Unitarian minister. She has one daughter, Althea.

Eileen Brennan Day is the Director of the School of Religion of the Unitarian Church in Arlington, Virginia. She was Director of the Church School of the Unitarian Church in Schenectady, New York for two years and has a B.S. degree in psychology from St. Lawrence University, Canton, New York. She is the wife of Dr. O. L. Day, a secondary school administrator, and has two young daughters, Bronwen and Harriet.

Janet Eaton Givens is a graduate of Queens College and Teachers College, Columbia University. She is teaching fourth grade in Westchester County, New York and previously taught first grade in Silver Spring, Maryland. Her previous writing has been for professional education journals.

Miriam Gorton was tragically killed in an automobile accident shortly after she started work on stories for this book, so that only one was finished. At the time of her death she was Director of Religious Education for the Universalist Church in Pasadena, California.

Marjorie Newlin Leaming was born in Hutsonville, Illinois. She holds a Master of Arts degree in Religious Education from the University of Chicago and Meadville Theological School. She has served as Director of Religious Education in the Evanston, Illinois, Unitarian Church, the Oak Park, Illinois, Universalist Church, and the Princeton, New Jersey, Unitarian Fellowship. At present she is the Director of the weekday nursery school of the Unitarian Society of Fort Wayne, Indiana, an interracial nursery school. Mrs. Leaming is the wife of a Unitarian minister, Rev. Hugo P. Leaming.

Lucile Lindberg is Coordinator of Student Teaching at Queens College in New York city. She received her doctorate from Teachers College, Columbia University. She has taught children of all ages in one-room schools, small towns, suburban areas, and cities. She has visited schools in South America, England, and the Soviet Union. Dr. Lindberg is an editor for the Council of Liberal Churches.

Margaret Ritchie is a graduate of the University of Rochester. She has taught in the Rochester public schools, at the secondary level, and in the adult evening program where she teaches courses in psychology. Her previous experience includes work as a general news reporter for the *Rochester Times Union* and several years with Bausch and Lomb Optical Company doing psychological testing. She has published articles in *Parents' Magazine, American Home, Better Homes and Gardens,* and *Sales Executive.* She is married to Donald Ritchie, a member of the faculty of the Rochester Institute of Technology, and is the mother of twin daughters, Peggy and Janet.

Dorothy T. Spoerl is an editor for the Council of Liberal Churches and an ordained Universalist minister. She has a Ph.D. in Psychology from Clark University and for eighteen years taught psychology at American International College in Springfield, Massachusetts. She recently resigned as chairman of the Psychology Department there to teach in a rural elementary school in Acworth, New Hampshire. She has one son, Walter.